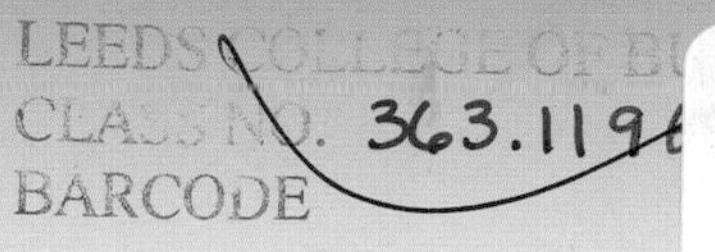

HSG149

Backs *for the* future

Safe manual handling in construction

HSE Books

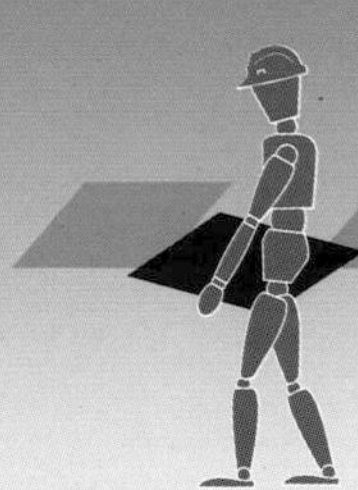

First published 2000

ISBN 0 7176 1122 1

This guidance is issued by the Health and Safety Executive. Following the guidance is not compulsory and you are free to take other action. But if you do follow the guidance you will normally be doing enough to comply with the law. Health and safety inspectors seek to secure compliance with the law and may refer to this guidance as illustrating good practice.

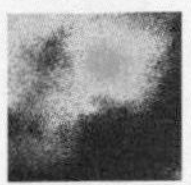

Contents

Preface ...iv

Introduction ...1

What is this book about? ...1

Who should read this book? ...1

Who is at risk? ...1

Why do these problems arise? ...1

Why do you need to take action? ...2

How to use this book ...2

Part 1: Designing, planning and managing manual handling - Who does what?

Designers ...5

Planning supervisors ...6

Principal contractors ...6

Contractors ...7

Information and training ...9

Manufacturers and suppliers ...10

Risk assessment ...10

Assessment of manual handling risks associated with blocklaying ...12

Key points for key people ...15

Part 2: Case studies

1 Redesigning roof supports ...20

2 Lifting roof trusses ...21

3 Handling roofing materials ...22

4 Loading out a roof ...23

5 Scaffolding ...24

6 Prefabrication of service distribution network ...25

7 Installation of plant ...26

8 Delivery of plaster bags ...27

9 Handling cement bags ...28

10 Fitting boiler to interior wall ...29

11 Fitting external guttering ...30

12 Placing concrete beams (lintels) ...31

13 Transporting materials using conveyors ...32

14 Bricklaying ...33

15 Handling of lead flashing ...34

16 Laying paving blocks ...35

17 Placing coping stones ...36

18 Placing kerbstones ...37

19 Handling site cabin sections ...38

20 Transporting materials over rough ground ...39

21 Moving plasterboard ...40

22 Handling of block pallets ...41

23 Prefabrication of service pipework ...42

24 Replacement of bridge, motorway and trunk road signs ...43

25 Placing road signs on a motorway ...44

26 Ground treatment of open-faced road tunnel ...45

27 Transporting LPG cylinders across carriageways ...46

Good ideas for tackling manual handling risks ...47

Appendix 1: Principal legal requirements ...50

Acknowledgements ...51

References ...52

Further reading and sources of advice ...52

Preface

Every year many construction workers are killed or injured as a result of their work; others suffer ill health, such as dermatitis, occupational deafness or musculoskeletal disorders. The construction industry's performance has improved over the past decade, but the rates of death, serious injury and ill health are still too high.

These deaths, injuries and ill health cause pain and suffering. They also cost money. A recent Health and Safety Executive (HSE) survey found that accidental loss wasted a significant amount of the tender price, even on a site which had no serious (reportable) accidents.

This book is part of HSE's revised series of health and safety guidance for construction. The series will be developed over the next few years, and will cover a number of key topics. The aim is to help all those involved in construction to identify the main causes of accidents and ill health and explain how to get rid of the hazards and control the risks. The guidance is simple but comprehensive. It will refer to other relevant publications so that you can build up a clear and comprehensive package.

Each publication will have general relevance to everyone involved in the construction process, from clients to designers, contractors, individual workers and safety representatives. However, some documents will be particularly relevant to specific groups, depending on the subject they address. All the new guidance will be identified with this logo.

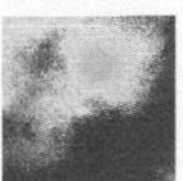

Introduction

What is this book about?

1 Construction work, by its very nature, involves many manual handling activities, which often contribute to musculoskeletal injuries, especially to the lower back. This book explains how manual handling risks can be reduced through better planning, control and management. It contains 27 case studies which describe real solutions that have been implemented on construction sites, showing effective ways in which manual handling risks have been reduced in practice. Many of the solutions are simple, cost-effective measures which were developed through co-operation between designers and contractors. Some examples of good ideas for reducing manual handling risks are given on page 47.

2 This guidance sets out the basic principles for dealing with manual handling risks. It also provides ideas for solutions to different manual handling problems. Not all the ideas will be relevant in all circumstances: different manual handling situations require different solutions, depending on the extent and nature of the risk.

Who should read this book?

3 Everyone involved in construction work has a role to play in managing manual handling risks. This guidance will, therefore, be of interest to:

- **(a)** clients;
- **(b)** designers;
- **(c)** planning supervisors;
- **(d)** principal contractors;
- **(e)** contractors;
- **(f)** employees and self-employed trades people.

Health and safety professionals and safety representatives should also find the guidance contained in the book helpful.

Who is at risk?

4 Manual handling is the major source of injury to construction workers. Every year, one-third of all construction industry accidents reported to HSE involve manual handling. These represent only a part of the actual problem, as many back injuries go unreported. Many construction workers experience symptoms of pain, aching and discomfort affecting their back, knees, neck and shoulders. These symptoms can be closely related to the type of manual handling activity; for example, work involving stooping and kneeling can lead to pain in the lower back and knees, while working with the arms raised above shoulder height can result in neck and shoulder pain. In each case long-term disability can result.

5 All these injuries are costly. Construction workers themselves bear the direct cost of lost earnings, pain and sometimes long-term incapacity. Costs to employers may be direct or indirect. Direct costs arise, for example, from loss of output, disruption to schedules, and sickness payments. Indirect costs may arise due to absence from work, training replacement workers, and resulting skills shortages. Insurance premiums may also be affected by manual handling injuries and compensation claims are becoming increasingly common. Improving manual handling operations can reduce these costs and provide several other benefits such as reduced fatigue, improved productivity and morale, less waste and smoother operations.

Why do these problems arise?

6 Several factors in construction can make manual handling tasks difficult. At present, construction workers are often required to:

- **(a)** support loads, often in awkward positions;

(b) move heavy materials;

(c) carry loads over rough, uneven ground or within buildings;

(d) carry out highly repetitive tasks;

(e) use handling equipment in difficult conditions, such as confined spaces.

Why do you need to take action?

7 The Manual Handling Operations Regulations 1992 (MHO) apply to all construction work. They set out a framework for employers to tackle the risk from manual handling. Under these Regulations, if employers cannot avoid manual handling where there is a risk of injury, they must assess their manual handling operations and take steps to reduce the risk of injury to the lowest level reasonably practicable.

An electrician, employed by a local council, seriously injured his lower back when he single-handedly unloaded a petrol-driven portable generator weighing 47 kg from a transit van. The council was prosecuted and found guilty of failing to make a manual handling assessment under regulation 4 of MHO.

8 The Construction (Design and Management) Regulations 1994 (CDM) apply to most construction work. Under CDM, everyone involved in the construction process must give adequate regard to health and safety. For manual handling this is especially appropriate for designers when considering specification of materials.

A client wanted the designer to produce a design with ornamental roof features. The initial intention was to produce the features from cast iron, lead and copper which would have required manual handling to lift them into position and fit them. Redesigning the features slightly, allowed them to be produced as a single, lightweight glass reinforced plastic (GRP) moulding which could be easily lifted and bolted into place. The reduction in weight substantially reduced the potential for serious manual handling injury.

How to use this book

9 Part 1 sets out the underlying principles for managing manual handling risks in construction. It describes the role that everyone involved in construction work needs to play to reduce manual handling risks and lists the key points for designers, planning supervisors, principal contractors, contractors, manufacturers and suppliers. It also provides an example of a manual handling risk assessment. Part 2 describes 27 actual case studies where manual handling risks were identified and real solutions implemented on construction sites. To help you identify which case studies may be of interest and relevance to you, Table 7 at the beginning of Part 2 lists the case studies and details the duty holders to whom they are particularly relevant. Several good ideas for reducing manual handling risks are also described on page 47.
A summary of the principal legal requirements relevant to manual handling is given in Appendix 1.

PART 1

Designing, planning and managing manual handling

Who does what?

10 Prevention is better than cure. Manual handling risks can often be avoided, or minimised, by carrying out the activity in a different way or by using different materials. Ways in which this can be done include:

(a) reprogramming the order of work, eg external guttering can be fitted before the scaffold is dropped, removing the need to carry materials up, and then work from, a ladder;

(b) using existing equipment on site to mechanically handle large loads, eg attaching a lifting jib to a telehandler, gives enough height to lift a full pack of roof trusses from ground to roof level, almost eliminating manual handling;

(c) changing the design of the materials used, eg specifying lower weight building blocks; while not getting rid of the risks from manual handling altogether, this certainly reduces them.

Designers

11 The way to avoid many risks from manual handling is during the design stage. Designers need to consider the manual handling risks that their designs may create and avoid them where possible. At the design stage, it may be possible to get rid of certain manual handling risks altogether by specifying in the design, those materials or components that are too large or heavy for manual handling. An example would be the specification of prefabricated units which need to be handled mechanically, rather than components which need manual assembly. Reducing manual handling risks through design not only brings health benefits, such as a reduction in the number of injuries to backs and limbs, but can also minimise the sort of disruption during construction that is illustrated by the following example.

Two performance specifications for an internal partition wall had to be met:

(a) effective sound insulation; and

(b) a fair face capable of giving a good finish when painted.

These were achieved by specifying concrete blocks which weighed 27 kg. The blocks were being laid by bricklayers working independently without mechanical assistance. The work was stopped by an HSE inspector and the designers were called to account for specifying heavy blocks. The project had a total value of £100 million and was already behind schedule. Within three days, two types of alternative block, weighing 13.5 kg and 16 kg, were found. These blocks fully met the two main criteria. Although slightly more expensive, the cost was more than recovered by an increased speed of laying the blocks.

12 Where manual handling cannot be avoided, designers can include features in their designs which will help with the management of manual handling on site. For example:

(a) specifying alternative lower weight materials where possible, eg using GRP ornamental features for buildings;

(b) making sure that designs allow enough space for access with mechanical handling equipment to where it is needed and for it to be used safely. Designs should also allow for access to internal spaces in buildings, for easier manual handling, or to permit use of mechanised handling aids;

(c) designing lifting points into the structure of building components so that cranes can be used to lift them into position;

(d) making sure that the design documentation

is clearly marked with the weights of materials or components.

13 Implications for manual handling, not just during the construction phase, but also during later maintenance, dismantling of plant or demolition, should not be forgotten. For example, during design it is important to consider access for the maintenance of services in areas such as plant rooms. Designers should also remember to take into account any maintenance and replacement requirements associated with the materials they specify.

14 Liaison with other designers, manufacturers and suppliers will help designers to keep abreast of new technological developments and available alternative materials that will get rid of or reduce the risks from manual handling. Designers can often, and where possible should, combine safety with aesthetics.

Planning supervisors

15 Planning supervisors should monitor the design proposals to ensure that manual handling risks arising from the design have been identified and avoided or reduced where possible. If the design does not appear to have taken manual handling risks into account, the planning supervisor should discuss this with the designer to see where design changes can be made. Discussions on managing the manual handling risks should take place as early in the project as possible. The planning supervisor should continue to maintain contact with the designer throughout the project to discuss appropriate ways to reduce manual handling risks through design. The planning supervisor should also encourage the early appointment of the principal contractor so that exchanges of information on proposed lifting processes, equipment capacity and availability are made easier.

16 The pre-tender health and safety plan, prepared by the planning supervisor, should contain information about the potential manual handling risks that may arise and should include:

(a) the weights of building materials to be used and any constraints on these;

(b) details of the environment in which the construction work will be done, which may cause problems for manual handling, for example:

- *(i)* presence of overhead cables which may restrict or rule out the use of mechanised lifting equipment;
- *(ii)* excessive gradients which may limit the use of handling aids for lifting and carrying materials;
- *(iii)* restrictions on access to work areas which may affect material lay-down and storage points;

(c) design features of the structure, which may make it difficult to use mechanical handling aids.

Principal contractors

17 Before construction starts, the construction health and safety plan, prepared by the principal contractor, should set out how manual handling will be managed in practice and detail site rules relevant to manual handling. In drawing up the plan, the principal contractor should consider ways of avoiding manual handling wherever possible during the construction phase. Even if manual handling cannot be avoided, it should be possible for the principal contractor to plan the work to reduce manual handling risk, eg by the way

in which work activities are sequenced, and examples of this are provided in the case studies in Part 2. In drawing up the plan, the principal contractor will need to liaise with the client, designer, planning supervisor and suppliers about alternative materials, and there can be considerable benefits from consulting the workforce and their safety representatives (see paragraph 32). The plan should include the principal contractor's and other contractors' risk assessments (see paragraphs 33-39) for manual handling that cannot be avoided. It can also include the following information on managing manual handling:

(a) A site layout plan detailing:

(i) routes to and from work areas (these may change as the site develops) to enable the safe movement of materials to deliver them as close as possible to their point of use. These routes should be marked, maintained and kept free of obstructions;

(ii) material delivery and storage areas which have sufficient space and lighting to allow for the safe movement of workers and handling equipment. The ground conditions of storage and material lay-down areas should be even and non-slippery to reduce the risk of slips, trips and falls. Poor ground can be made good using a covering of crushed hard core. Proper phasing of the delivery of materials will help to make the best use of site storage areas.

(b) Site rules:

(i) handling of materials, eg all bagged products weighing more than 25 kg should be mechanically handled;

(ii) good housekeeping - a good standard of general site tidiness should be maintained to keep work areas free of obstructions which may prevent the safe movement of materials.

(c) Training and information:

(i) site induction which covers site-specific information on aspects of safe handling and moving loads, including selection of the right equipment for the job.

(d) Lifting and handling equipment:

(i) provision of equipment (where applicable) for lifting and handling. This includes both mechanical and non-mechanical handling equipment, where it is located, its maintenance and who to see to ask for it.

18 The detail on managing manual handling contained in the construction phase health and safety plan will be of little use unless it is carried out. Avoid last-minute changes to the work, wherever possible, as they can cause confusion and introduce manual handling risks. Principal contractors should liaise with contractors on manual handling issues throughout the construction phase. They should manage putting the plan into action by checking that people keep to the plan and, where necessary, making sure that they do so.

19 Much of the information contained in the following section on contractors' duties is relevant for the principal contractor.

Contractors

20 Contractors need to ensure that they and their employees follow the principal contractor's construction phase health and safety plan. Contractors will need to assess those activities where there are remaining manual handling risks that have not been removed or avoided through design. In most cases, manual handling assessments are not difficult. More detailed information on manual handling assessment and an example of how to assess the manual handling risks associated with blocklaying is provided at the end of Part 1 (see paragraphs 34-38).

21 Contractors can use risk assessment (see paragraph 33) as a basis for deciding on what action to take to reduce the risk of injury. The assessment should have identified the parts of the handling activity that pose risks to employees and the cause of those risks.

22 When assessing manual handling risks, contractors should always ask the people who do the job. They know what the problems are, and involving them in the development of solutions to manual handling problems often leads to better solutions which are more readily accepted.

23 The contractor should give some thought to the selection of both mechanical and non-mechanical lifting and handling equipment for the type of material being used. There is a wide variety of equipment available, for example:

(a) rough terrain fork-lift trucks can be used for unloading materials and to lift and move loads, such as brick packs, cement and aggregates around the site;

(b) cranes, powered and hand-operated hoists can be used for lifting awkward loads, such as roof trusses and rolls of roofing felt, from one level to another;

(c) scissor lifts, although mainly used as access equipment, can take small tools and lighter loads, such as bags of fixings, from the ground to higher levels (if they are used for heavier loads it is essential that their suitability for this purpose is checked first);

(d) trolleys, sack and pallet trucks, wheelbarrows and conveyors can reduce the amount of effort needed to move any load horizontally;

(e) telescopic handlers are particularly useful for delivering bricks to higher levels;

(f) chutes can be used to move loads from one place to another;

(g) devices such as compressed air equipment and suction pads can help with handling a load, such as glass or plasterboard, that is difficult to grasp.

24 In general, the actions the contractor should take to reduce the risk of injury from essential manual handling operations are those which will result in:

(a) changing the layout of the job so that workers can lift and move loads at more favourable heights;

(b) reducing the amount of bending, stooping, stretching, pushing and pulling to make the job easier to perform;

(c) reducing the number of times a job has to be done;

(d) reducing the amount of effort required from an individual, by introducing team lifting, where this is appropriate.

25 Ensure that the principal contractor's site layout plan sets out arrangements for the delivery and storage of materials. The following ideas on the delivery and storage of materials on site can help in reducing manual handling risks:

(a) Have materials delivered straight to the person needing them and place them as close as possible to where they will be used to help avoid the need for double handling; for example, concrete can be pumped or cement bags delivered straight to the mixing area.

(b) Phase the delivery of materials to make the best use of site storage areas.

(c) Ensure that areas designated for storage of materials are big enough for their purpose; cramped working conditions increase manual handling risks.

(d) Store materials in easy reach and at a proper height, ie above ground level and below eye level.

(e) Where site roads exist, move materials around on fork-lift trucks. Make sure routes used for carrying materials are marked, maintained and kept free of obstructions.

(f) Maintain good ground conditions where main storage areas and material lay-down areas are sited; uneven and slippery ground increases the risk of slips, trips and falls.

(g) Clean lay-down areas often result in significantly reduced wastage.

26 Except for minor roof work involving only small amounts of materials, which can be safely carried without causing injury, mechanical lifting aids should be used to deliver materials to roof level. These may range from a simple gin wheel to a powered hoist. In most cases, carrying materials to roof level in hods should not be necessary.

27 Contractors should make sure that mechanical equipment for handling materials is delivered to site in good time and that the site has been prepared for it. All equipment used for lifting should be in good condition and only used by competent operators. Remember that the use of mechanical handling equipment can create different kinds of risks. It will need maintenance and the law requires lifting machines and lifting tackle to be examined. Workers will need to be trained or instructed in how to operate mechanical handling equipment safely. Contractors will need to consider the co-ordination of site activities, so that those involved in lifting operations do not endanger other workers and vice versa.

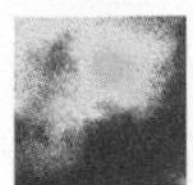

Information and training

28 All contractors are responsible for ensuring that their workers receive instruction and training in safe manual handling. This should be seen as part of a safe system of work and not as a substitute for it. Training is an important aspect of reducing the risk of manual handling injury. Contractors should also make sure that their supervisors and workers understand how the control measures for reducing the risks from manual handling have been designed to ensure safety.

29 Employees need to have a clear understanding of:

(a) the risks to their health and safety from manual handling;

(b) how to recognise potentially hazardous manual handling operations;

(c) how to deal with unfamiliar manual handling operations;

(d) the proper use of manual handling equipment;

(e) the proper use of personal protective equipment;

(f) the importance of good housekeeping;

(g) good manual handling techniques;

(h) duties on employees to use the systems of work provided to reduce the risk of injury.

30 Any instruction or training should be relevant to the handling situations that are likely to be met on site. Formal training is ideal, but other methods such as site induction, tool-box talks, posters, etc, can be equally effective in getting the 'safe handling' message across. Whatever form the instruction takes, the important point to make is **before lifting always think about how to reduce the amount of effort involved and use whatever means are available to make the task easier.**

31 As well as training workers in safe lifting techniques, any manual handling instruction should highlight the many different approaches that can play a part in reducing, or getting rid of, the risk of injury. People need to be kept up to date and given instruction when new techniques or lifting aids are introduced.

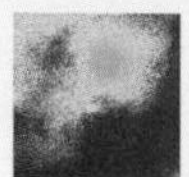

Manufacturers and suppliers

32 Manufacturers and suppliers of construction materials also have an important part to play in helping to reduce manual handling risks on construction sites. By considering how materials are packaged, secured and marked, they can reduce the weight or bulkiness of a load, making it easier to handle. For instance:

(a) reducing the weight of bagged products from 50 kg to 25 kg will significantly reduce the risk of back injury;

(b) providing suitable handles, hand grips or handholds on the load will make it easier to control; position handles or hand grips at the load's centre of gravity to enable the bulk of the weight to be held close to the body;

(c) securing the load so that it does not shift unexpectedly when being handled; for example using packing material, or adequate strapping, will not only make a load easier to handle, but may also reduce damage to contents;

(d) marking the load to indicate its weight and (particularly for asymmetrical loads) indicating the centre of gravity will make it easier to decide whether it can be lifted by hand and how best to lift it;

(e) including lifting points on the load will make it easier to lift by mechanical means - it is important that lifting points are positioned so that loads are stable when lifted.

A contractor building a large leisure development approached the architect to try to get the specification for large building blocks weighing 35 kg changed. However, all options for alternative blocks had been considered and these large blocks were required for their acoustic attenuation properties. The initial response of the contractor was to use a two-man lift to lay the blocks, but following discussion with the block supplier it was agreed that blocks could be made to special order, half the size and weight of the blocks originally specified. These lighter square-shaped blocks were much preferred by the workforce as they could be laid by a single person, were easier to align and could be laid at a faster rate.

Risk assessment

33 When assessing the manual handling risk you need to consider the different characteristics that make up the activity. These are:

(a) **task**;

(b) **load**;

(c) **work environment**;

(d) **individual capability**.

Each of these on its own can have an effect, although, more commonly, it will be a combination of these factors that influences the manual handling risk. When carrying out a manual handling assessment, it is important that the activity is taken as a whole and the interaction between these four characteristics is considered. Consultation with workers or their safety representatives, who have past experience of such work, can be of considerable assistance when identifying manual handling risks. Table 1 highlights what needs to be considered when making an assessment.

Table 1 **What to consider when assessing manual handling risk**

Task

- The nature of the task: find out how much reaching, bending, stooping, stretching and twisting is involved.
- The position of the load relative to the handler is important in determining the degree of control and effort required to do the task. If a load has to be lifted above head height, eg when installing a lintel or fixing plaster-board to a ceiling, then the degree of control and effort needed will be greater than if the activity were carried out at waist height.
- The frequency and duration of the handling are important in determining the degree of risk. Where there are repetitive lifting operations combined with repeated bending, twisting and reaching over a period of time, the effect of all these tasks added together significantly increases the likelihood of injury, eg in bricklaying.

Load

- The nature of the load: is it heavy, bulky, hard to grasp? The weight, size, shape and stability of the load all contribute to the degree of control and effort needed for the activity.

Work environment

- The nature of the working environment: is it hot, cold, windy, poorly lit? Are there slopes, uneven ground, poor access arrangements?
- Constraints on posture (such as plumbers may experience in confined spaces) increase the degree of control and effort needed for the task, increasing the risk of injury.
- Poor ground conditions make slips and trips more likely.
- Carrying items on slopes requires greater effort than carrying on the level.
- Manual handling should be done from a scaffold, not from a ladder.
- Placing light materials such as roofing sheets in windy conditions makes the manual handling task more difficult.

Individual capability

- Does the job require someone of unusual height or strength? Does the individual have an existing health problem which increases the risk?
- An individual's age, strength, level of skill and experience will affect how much a person can safely handle.

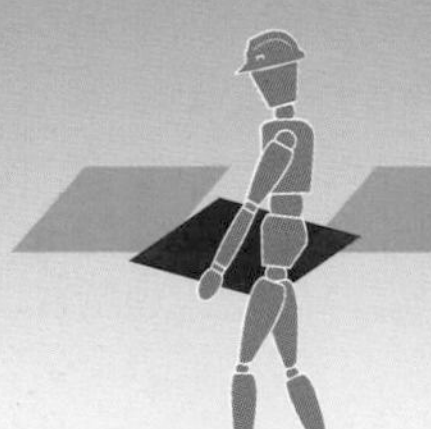

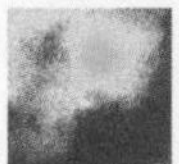

Assessment of manual handling risks associated with blocklaying

34 Figure 1 is an example of a risk assessment for blocklaying. During building of a large supermarket, heavy blocks weighing 32 kg were being manually laid to form the inner skin of the walls. Using a simple, pictorial form the blocklaying activity was assessed by ticking the appropriate 'yes/no' box for each of the different factors which needed to be considered: the way the task was done, the load to be handled, the work environment and the individual's capability to do the job. Boxes ticked 'yes' indicated areas for improvement. The control measures suggested at the bottom of the assessment form were designed to tackle these areas. The completed assessment is shown in paragraph 36.

35 Figure 1 shows that the single-handed repetitive manual handling of blocks weighing 32 kg carries a potential risk of injury to the worker. The combination of the weight of the blocks, the site conditions and the way the job was organised, all contribute to the risk.

36 Use the assessment as a basis for determining what action to take. In the example shown in Figure 1, the following actions which could make the job easier to do have been identified:

(a) discuss with the planning supervisor and the designer (via the principal contractor) the selection of the blocks. Check whether lighter blocks could be used (the designer should have already considered this at the outset but it is worth checking as they may not always be aware of the availability of lighter blocks);

(b) investigate the use of a mechanical lifting device to avoid the need to manually handle the blocks;

(c) use a non-mechanical block lifting device;

(d) select blocks with handholds, where possible;

(e) arrange for the blocks to placed alongside the trench to reduce carrying distance from the lay-down area to their point of use;

(f) improve the working environment by using in-trench boarding to reduce the risk of slips and trips on the uneven ground;

(g) provide appropriate gloves to protect the handler from cuts, bruises and scratches. Gloves may also improve the handler's grip on the load;

(h) improve the handling skills of workers through manual handling skills training.

37 Using risk assessment to highlight potential risks means that changes can be made to an activity to help prevent a manual handling injury from happening.

38 The simple example shown in Figure 1 provides a good starting point for addressing manual handling risks. A blank version of Figure 1 is on page 14, which you can photocopy and fill out. There are other types of checklists available to help you make an assessment but they all cover the same points. An example of a checklist form can be found in HSE's publication *Manual handling. Manual Handling Operations Regulations 1992, Guidance on Regulations*.

39 For some manual handling situations you may require the support of an ergonomist or other occupational health professional to help you. Information about how to obtain professional help can be found in the HSE booklet *Selecting a health and safety consultancy* or for a list of professional ergonomists write to The Ergonomics Society, Devonshire House, Devonshire Square, Loughborough, Leics LE11 3DW. Tables 2-6 summarise the key points for designers, planning supervisors, principal contractors, contractors, and manufacturers and suppliers, respectively.

Figure 1

Manual handling operations record

Mark boxes as appropriate. Every activity must be marked

Company *Made Up Ltd* **Project/premises** *Supermarket site* **Activity** *Blocklaying*

Materials to be handled *32 kg blocks* **Hazardous contents** *None* **Locations** *Ground level*

Can manual handling be eliminated? *No*

TASK

Item	YES	NO
STOOPING	☑	☐
LIFTING HIGH	☐	☑
LIFTING LOW	☑	☐
HANDLING WHILE SEATED	☐	☑
REPETITION	☑	☐
REACHING HIGH	☑	☐
REACHING LOW	☑	☐
CARRYING	☑	☐
TWISTING	☑	☐
BENDING SIDEWAYS	☐	☑
PUSHING	☐	☑
PULLING	☐	☑

LOAD

Item	YES	NO
BULKY/ UNWIELDY	☑	☐
DIFFICULT TO GRIP	☑	☐
HOT	☐	☑
COLD	☐	☑
HEAVY	☑	☐
LIGHT	☐	☑
SHARP/ ABRASIVE	☑	☐
UNSTABLE	☐	☑
ECCENTRIC SHAPE	☐	☑

ENVIRON

Item	YES	NO
HOT	☑	☐
COLD	☐	☑
HUMID	☑	☐
WINDY	☐	☑
DUSTY	☑	☐
NOISY	☐	☑
VIBRATING	☐	☑
OBSTRUCTIONS	☐	☑
STEPS	☐	☑
CONFINED SPACES	☑	☐
SLOPES	☑	☐
UNEVEN SURFACES	☑	☐

PERSON

Item	YES	NO
NEED FOR UNUSUAL STRENGTH, ETC	☑	☐
TRAINING REQUIRED	☑	☐
PPE TO BE WORN	☑	☐
18 - 55 YEARS?	☑	☐
MEDICAL CONDITION OR HISTORY	☐	☑

Control measures

1) *Discuss selection of blocks with designer (via principal contractor). Lighter blocks may be available.*
2) *Investigate use of mechanical lifting device to avoid the need for manual handling of blocks*
3) *Use a non-mechanical block lifting device if (2) above is not practical.*
4) *Discuss using blocks with handholds with designer (via principal contractor).*
5) *Place blocks nearer to their point of use to reduce carrying distance.*
6) *Investigate use of intrench boarding to improve ground conditions.*
7) *Provide gloves to protect hands from cuts and scratches and to improve grip.*
8) *Arrange refresher training in manual handling skills.*

Assessor *E.R. Gonomic* **Date** *1/2/34* **Received by** *M. Handling* **Date** *2/2/34*

Manual handling operations record

Mark boxes as appropriate. Every activity must be marked

Company ______ **Project/premises** ______ **Activity** ______

Materials to be handled ______ **Hazardous contents** ______ **Locations** ______

Can manual handling be eliminated? ______

TASK	STOOPING YES ❑ NO ❑	LIFTING HIGH YES ❑ NO ❑	LIFTING LOW YES ❑ NO ❑	HANDLING WHILE SEATED YES ❑ NO ❑	REPETITION YES ❑ NO ❑	REACHING HIGH YES ❑ NO ❑	REACHING LOW YES ❑ NO ❑	CARRYING YES ❑ NO ❑	TWISTING YES ❑ NO ❑	BENDING SIDEWAYS YES ❑ NO ❑	PUSHING YES ❑ NO ❑	PULLING YES ❑ NO ❑
LOAD	BULKY/ UNWIELDY YES ❑ NO ❑	DIFFICULT TO GRIP YES ❑ NO ❑	HOT YES ❑ NO ❑	COLD YES ❑ NO ❑	HEAVY YES ❑ NO ❑	LIGHT YES ❑ NO ❑	SHARP/ ABRASIVE YES ❑ NO ❑	UNSTABLE YES ❑ NO ❑	ECCENTRIC SHAPE YES ❑ NO ❑			
ENVIRON	HOT YES ❑ NO ❑	COLD YES ❑ NO ❑	HUMID YES ❑ NO ❑	WINDY YES ❑ NO ❑	DUSTY YES ❑ NO ❑	NOISY YES ❑ NO ❑	VIBRATING YES ❑ NO ❑	OBSTRUCTIONS YES ❑ NO ❑	STEPS YES ❑ NO ❑	CONFINED SPACES YES ❑ NO ❑	SLOPES YES ❑ NO ❑	UNEVEN SURFACES YES ❑ NO ❑
PERSON	NEED FOR UNUSUAL STRENGTH, ETC YES ❑ NO ❑	TRAINING REQUIRED YES ❑ NO ❑	PPE TO BE WORN YES ❑ NO ❑	18 - 55 YEARS? YES ❑ NO ❑	MEDICAL CONDITION OR HISTORY YES ❑ NO ❑							

Control measures

Assessor ______ **Date** ______ **Received by** ______ **Date** ______

Courtesy of Mace Ltd

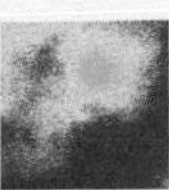

Key points for key people

Table 2 **Key points for designers**

- Identify the manual handling risks your design/specification will create for construction workers
- Avoid manual handling risks where possible
- Specify either lower weight products that can be easily handled or items that are so large/heavy they have to be handled mechanically
- Design for the use of mechanical handling aids where appropriate
- Design in lifting points to enable cranes to be used
- Consider manual handling risks involved in maintenance, dismantling and demolition
- Liaise with manufacturers and suppliers about available alternative materials that will help to reduce manual handling
- Clearly mark design documentation with the weights of the products

Table 3 **Key points for planning supervisors**

- Monitor design proposals for manual handling risks
- Consider early on in the project how manual handling risks can be managed
- Maintain contact with the designer throughout the project to discuss how to reduce manual handling risks through design
- Include information about the potential for manual handling risks in the pre-tender health and safety plan
- Encourage early appointment of the principal contractor to facilitate the exchange of information on proposed lifting processes, equipment capacity and availability

Table 4 **Key points for principal contractors**

- Plan to avoid manual handling wherever possible during the construction phase
- Make sure manual handling activities which cannot be avoided have been properly assessed
- Plan the sequencing of work activities to allow for the reduction of manual handling risk
- Liaise with the client, designer and planning supervisor as early as possible about alternative materials and with contractors on manual handling issues
- Plan and manage site layout and storage areas, allowing for the use of handling equipment
- Make site rules for managing manual handling
- Monitor and make sure site rules are followed
- Use site inductions to inform and instruct workers in safe handling
- Consult the workforce and their safety representatives

Table 5 **Key points for contractors**
■ Assess manual handling risks
■ Reduce manual handling risks by:
• mechanising the task
• improving the layout of the task, or the way it is done
• changing the characteristics of the load
• improving the working environment
• instructing people in safe handling techniques
• supervising the work to ensure safe systems are implemented
■ Plan and manage the way materials are delivered and distributed on site
■ Make sure that appropriate handling equipment is available and that it is properly maintained
■ Co-operate/liaise with the principal contractor on manual handling issues
■ Remember to ask the people who do the job and their safety representatives

Table 6 **Key points for manufacturers and suppliers**
■ Package materials to reduce the weight or bulkiness of the load
■ Provide suitable handles, hand grips or handholds on the load, positioned at the load's centre of gravity
■ Secure the load so that it does not shift unexpectedly when being handled
■ Mark the load to indicate its weight and, where practicable, indicate its centre of gravity
■ Include mechanical lifting points on the load, positioned so that the load area is stable when lifted

PART 2

Case studies

Table 7 List of case studies and the duty holders to whom they apply

No	Case study	Page no	Duty holder: Client	Designer	Planning supervisor	Principal contractor	Contractor
1	Redesigning roof supports	20	✓	✓	✓	✓	
2	Lifting roof trusses	21				✓	✓
3	Handling roofing materials	22					✓
4	Loading out a roof	23				✓	✓
5	Scaffolding	24		(✓)*			✓
6	Prefabrication of service distribution network	25	✓	✓	✓	✓	
7	Installation of plant	26	✓	✓	✓	✓	✓
8	Delivery of plaster bags	27		(✓)	(✓)	✓	✓
9	Handling cement bags	28				✓	✓
10	Fitting boiler to interior wall	29		(✓)		✓	✓
11	Fitting external guttering	30		(✓)*	(✓)	✓	✓
12	Placing concrete beams (lintels)	31		(✓)	(✓)	(✓)	✓
13	Transporting materials using conveyors	32				(✓)	✓
14	Bricklaying	33		(✓)*		✓	✓
15	Handling of lead flashing	34				(✓)	✓
16	Laying paving blocks	35				(✓)	✓
17	Placing coping stones	36				✓	✓
18	Placing kerbstones	37					✓
19	Handling site cabin sections	38				(✓)	✓
20	Transporting materials over rough ground	39	(✓)		(✓)	(✓)	✓
21	Moving plasterboard	40				✓	✓
22	Handling of block pallets	41				✓	✓
23	Prefabrication of service pipework	42	✓	✓	✓	✓	
24	Replacement of bridge, motorway and trunk road signs	43	(✓)	(✓)	(✓)	✓	✓
25	Placing road signs on a motorway	44	(✓)	✓	(✓)	✓	✓
26	Ground treatment of open-faced road tunnel	45		(✓)	✓	✓	✓
27	Transporting LPG cylinders across carriageways	46				✓	✓
	Good ideas for tackling manual handling risks	47	✓	✓	✓	✓	✓

(✓) Likely to be of additional interest to duty holder.

(✓)* Temporary works designer

CASE STUDY 1

Redesigning roof supports

Task

A house-building company used steel beams to support the roof trusses in the production of a popular house style.

Problem

The beams were manually lifted and placed by hand. Lack of space ruled out the use of a crane. The company wished to reduce the manual handling risk without changing the external appearance of the roof.

Finding a solution

The company's technical design department contacted the designers who had originally designed the roof truss system. Some ideas for solutions were suggested by the designers, but they still required the use of a steel beam. The manufacturers of the roof truss were contacted and together they were able to develop a new design using trusses which did not require any steelwork. These roof trusses could be positioned by telehandler. The additional cost for the trusses was offset by savings on the steel beam and associated items such as steel lintels, pad stones and reinforced brickwork. The external appearance of the roof was unchanged.

Results

The manual handling and other safety risks associated with the task have been greatly reduced. Additional cost savings have also been realised from the design change.

The case study emphasises the importance of design in reducing manual handling risks. However, where design constraints do not allow for a reduction in the weight of a load, mechanical handling should be considered. Designers should be aware of the need for adequate space for using mechanical lifting devices when designing the layout of a site.

This is a good example of designers, contractors and manufacturers working well together to address manual handling problems.

CASE STUDY 2

Lifting roof trusses

Task

On a housing development site, roof trusses were being placed in position. Workers had to lift the trusses by hand from ground level up to the point of fixing at roof level. This task was performed by two workers, one on the ground who lifted and pushed a truss up towards a second worker standing on the platform at roof level. The truss was then pulled up into position.

Problem

The large trusses were difficult to manoeuvre and the awkward working positions assumed by the workers to push and pull the trusses into position presented a high risk of injury. In addition, the scaffold handrail had been removed in order to get the trusses into position, posing a very real risk of falling from that section of the scaffold. Although this method was considered time-efficient for lifting small roof trusses, it still carried a risk of injury which was greatly increased when trying to lift larger trusses in the same way.

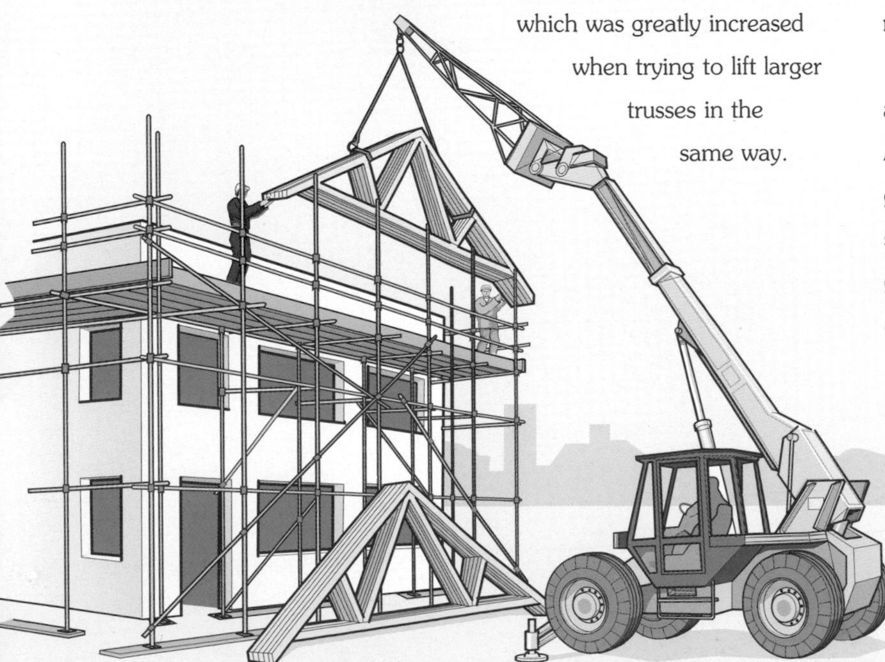

Finding a solution

Recognising this, the company arranged to fit a lifting jib attachment to a telehandler. This arrangement provided enough height to lift a full pack of roof trusses safely from ground level, over the handrail, and onto the working platform. The jibs were readily available to hire or buy and the telehandlers were already being used on site. The company's site rules were revised to include the use of a telehandler to lift trusses up to roof level.

Results

This simple adaptation of lifting equipment which was already available on the site effectively got rid of manual handling and the risk of injury from this task. The lifting jib attachment was hired by the company at relatively low cost. Revising the site rules ensured that everyone involved in this task would use the telehandler to lift the trusses. The risk of falling from the working platform was also reduced as the handrail remained in place.

A more favourable approach might be to assemble the roof, or sections of it, on the ground. A telehandler can be used to transport trusses at ground level. Such prefabrication allows completed sections or whole roofs to be craned into place, getting rid of the need for manual handling as well as the need for work at height.

Caution: Make sure that any equipment used for lifting is operated within its safe lifting capacity. Always refer to the manufacturer's information.

CASE STUDY 3

Handling roofing materials

Task

An old corrugated iron roof on a large storage facility was worn out and had to be replaced. New roofing panels of composite material were to be used for the new roof. The panels varied in length to over 10 m and weighed about 100 kg. The size and location of the building meant that a crane could not be used to place the panels. Instead, the panels had to be placed manually and access was limited to the valley gutters. The panels were taken up to roof level by a hoist and then carried by two roof workers a distance of up to 90 m before being installed.

Problem

The size and weight of the panels, the distance they had to be carried and the restricted access route together posed a high risk of injury to the roof workers.

Finding a solution

The roof workers recognised the difficulties associated with this task and gave some thought to identifying a simple but effective solution. They designed a trolley, of simple construction, which would support the panels and travel easily up and down the valley gutters.

Results

The high risk of injury from carrying the panels was significantly reduced by using the valley gutter trolley. The cost of constructing the trolley was small, especially in terms of the overall cost of the contract. The roof workers were able to work more quickly and so the overall load-out rate was increased. The development of a simple, inexpensive and effective means of reducing the manual handling risks associated with this job clearly illustrates the benefits of consulting the people who do the job and allowing them to think about and develop their own solutions.

CASE STUDY 4

Loading out a roof

Task

A contractor was building two-storey, timber-framed houses on a small reclamation site with very limited storage space and restricted access. The roofing subcontractor on this site had not costed for the use of any kind of hoist because his employees had traditionally loaded out roofs using ladders and hods to take the tiles from the ground to roof level.

Problem

The repetitive carrying of a loaded hod up a ladder presents risks from both manual handling and falling. Both the weight of the load and the poor working positions of the roof workers to enable them to get up the ladder combined to pose a high risk of injury. The limited storage space on site meant that when the tiles were delivered, access to the site was blocked. Because getting the tiles up to the roof in this manner was a slow process, access to the site remained blocked for a considerable amount of time, causing problems and frustration for other contractors on the site.

Finding a solution

The principal contractor for the development required the roofing subcontractor to assess the manual handling risks associated with loading out the roof, and to introduce measures that would reduce the risk of injury as much as possible. The roofing subcontractor concluded from his assessment that the job carried a high risk of injury when done in this way. He investigated a range of options and found that the most cost-effective way of providing a solution was to hire an inclined hoist. After being instructed in the use of the hoist, the roof workers used it to load out the roofs.

Results

Manual handling was greatly reduced when the hoist was used. The roofs were loaded out more safely in a third of the time without the need for additional manpower. The increased speed of loading out the roofs meant that the tiles were not left to block the site access as they had done previously, improving relationships on site between contractors.

CASE STUDY 5

Scaffolding

Task

A scaffolding company was erecting a curved scaffold for a new building project using conventional steel scaffold and wooden boards. Two trained scaffolders were working for 3-4 hours at a time from an unstable base comprising two scaffold boards.

Problem

Scaffold tubes are heavy and unwieldy and it requires a lot of effort to control and place them precisely. Placing the tubes requires a good deal of manoeuvring of the tube and reaching above head height. To carry out this task, workers have to put up with poor working positions with much twisting and stretching. In addition, the repetitive nature of securing the tubes in place causes additional strain on the arms and, in particular, the wrists of workers.

Finding a solution

Recognising the risk, the company decided to look at how the materials were moved to their actual point of use. After consulting the scaffold designer about the weight-loading restrictions of the scaffold, they constructed purpose-built crates in which the bundles of tubes were placed. The crates were then mechanically lifted, by telehandler, to their point of use. The scaffolders were also given gloves to wear which helped increase their grip on the materials. The gloves also served as a protective measure against skin damage.

Results

These inexpensive, easy-to-put-into-practice solutions successfully reduced the manual handling risks to the scaffolders.

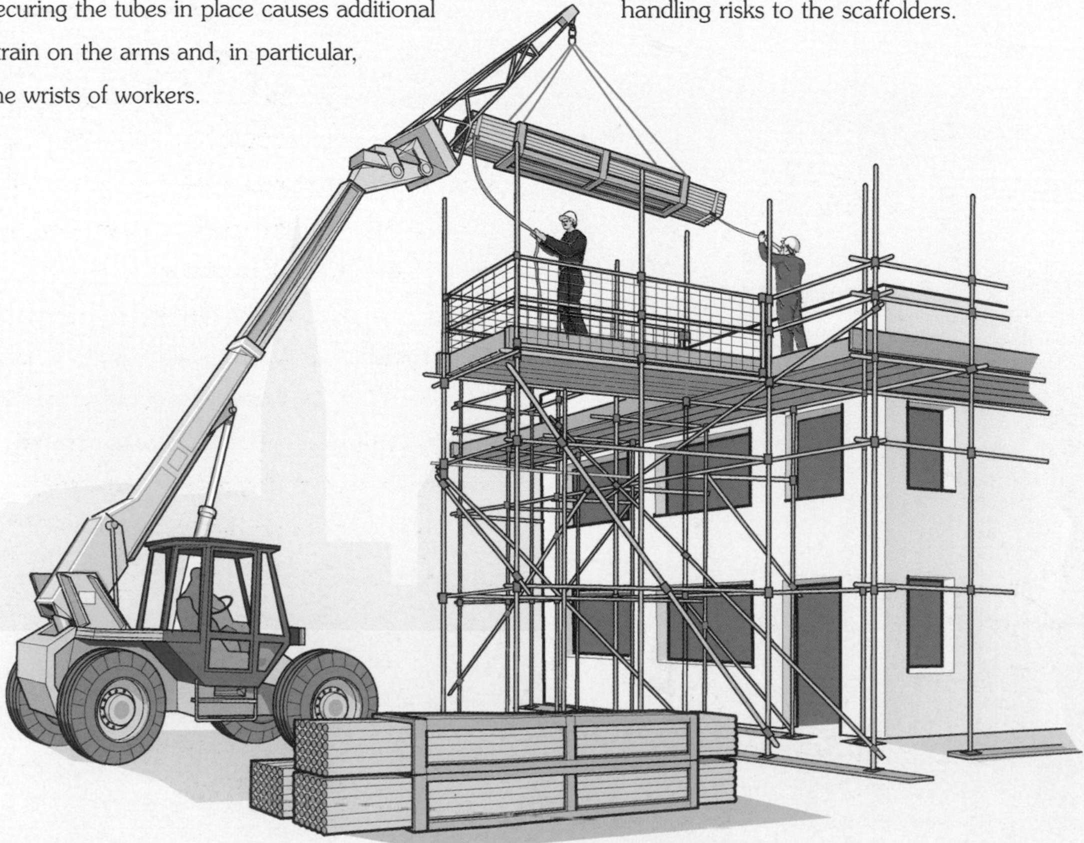

CASE STUDY 6

Prefabrication of service distribution network

Task

A client required the full replacement of a service distribution network including all pipework, ductwork and cable trays in a tall office block. The services had to be ceiling-mounted.

Problem

The physical layout of the building, restricted access and a lack of storage space created difficulties. Workers carried materials to the work area for storage. They installed the services using floor-to-ceiling scaffolding. This presented a manual handling risk because of the poor postures required to fix the load into position overhead at ceiling height.

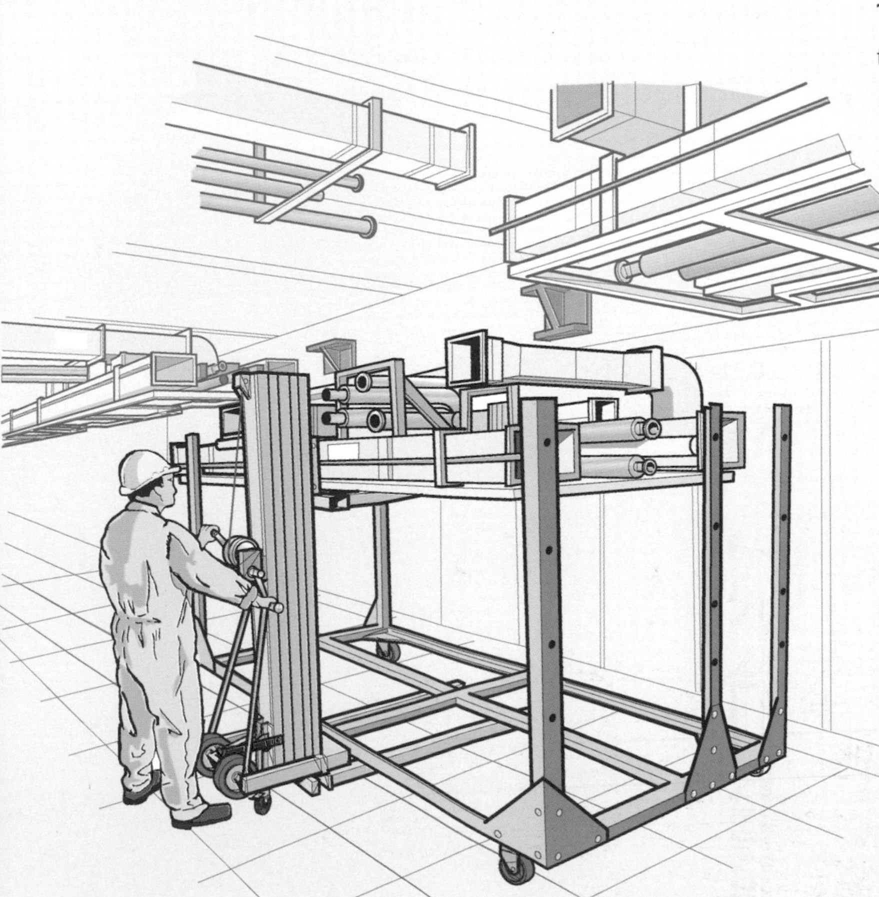

Finding a solution

The principal contractor reviewed the initial design and planning for the job. Together with the designer, a prefabrication process was selected. The services were assembled off-site in the form of caged modules resting on benches at waist height. The modules weighed approximately 300 kg each and were delivered to site in specially designed bogies. Each module was raised to ceiling level using a hand-operated lift truck and fixed in position, connected and tested. Deliveries were programmed on a 'just-in-time' basis.

Results

The design change to prefabricated modules and the use of mechanical aids to position them, significantly reduced the risk of manual handling injury, enabling employees to maintain an improved posture when connecting and testing the units.

Other benefits included:

(a) a considerable saving in time;

(b) no storage space required;

(c) no full floor scaffold required;

(d) improved consistency and quality of work.

This case study illustrates how changing the size of the load can avoid the need for manual handling (in this instance by making the load so heavy it needs to be mechanically handled to move it).

CASE STUDY 7

Installation of plant

Task

Workers had to erect a large steam boiler which required connection of finned tubes between the top and bottom drum which were set vertically apart at a distance of about 20 m.

Problem

The tube bundles were stored away from the installation point and were moved by crane to their point of use. Although individual tubes were lifted up by a powered chain block to their attachment point, they had to be manually inserted into the top and bottom of each drum. The process had to repeated for over 500 tubes and normally took a team of nine men four weeks to complete.

Finding a solution

Complete modules were built off-site and transported to site by a specialist haulier. The modules were fitted with a specially designed lifting frame and lifted into place mechanically before being fitted by a team of five workers.

Results

The design change to units which were assembled off-site removed the need for manual handling. There was also a saving in time and personnel with considerably fewer workers required to complete the task. This case study illustrates how changing the size of the load can avoid the need for manual handling (in this instance making the load so heavy it needs to be mechanically handled to move it).

CASE STUDY 8

Delivery of plaster bags

Task

Plastering is normally done midway through or at the end of a project, and often considerable numbers of plaster bags need to be delivered to mixing areas.

Problem

On a building project, bags were delivered after the external walls and roof of the building had been completed. It was difficult to set up mechanical handling aids such as hoists, to move the bags into the building. The bags had to be carried through doorways, along corridors and up stairwells.

Finding a solution

Delivering the bags before the external walls and roof were complete allowed the use of mechanical handling aids, such as hoists, to move the bags into the building. Simple non-mechanical handling aids, such as wheeled pallet trucks, could then be used to take several bags at a time from the hoist to storage areas on completed floors of the building. Covering the plaster while it was being stored there kept it dry. Storing bags in a locked store when not in use, rather than on the floor of the building, will help to reduce the potential for theft.

Results

A simple change in the planned programming of works on a site enabled both mechanical and non-mechanical handling equipment to be used, almost getting rid of the need for manual handling. There are no costs associated with this kind of change. Liaison with workers and other contractors ensured the change was easy to make and readily accepted by all concerned.

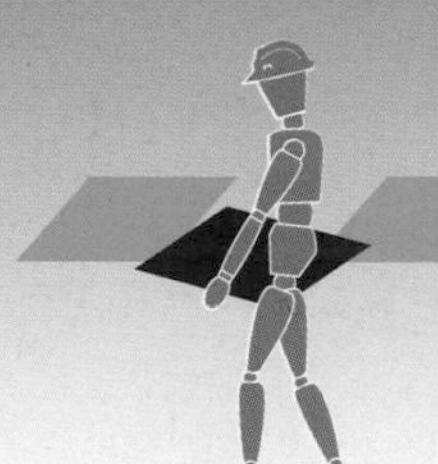

CASE STUDY 9

Handling cement bags

Task

On a house-building site it was necessary to handle large quantities of bagged materials, particularly cement. At one location, a labourer had to manually unload 50 kg bags of cement from a delivery lorry and carry them to a storage shed where they were stacked at ground level. When needed, the bags had to be lifted from a low position and carried to the cement mixer. This could involve the labourer carrying a 50 kg bag about 18 m across very slippery ground several times a day. To load the mixer, the labourer had to split the bag in two with a shovel and lift one half from ground level up to waist height and pour its contents into the mixer.

Problem

In general, if workers do not apply correct lifting techniques there may be a risk of back injury from the weight of the bags and from lifting them from a low position to waist height. The labourers on the project considered this to be a heavy manual handling task and, as a result, many complained that they suffered from various muscular aches and pains. There was also considerable wastage of cement from this method of use of 50 kg bags.

Finding a solution

The building company reviewed its purchasing policy for cement bags and opted to use 25 kg bags of cement which were readily available from the suppliers. In addition, they made sure the labourers were instructed in correct manual handling techniques.

Results

The manual handling risks associated with this task were reduced. Cost savings of approximately £1500 per year from reduced wastage of cement were realised. There were fewer complaints of back pain from labourers.

Reducing the weight of the bags, combined with a reminder of good manual handling techniques, is a simple and effective way of reducing the manual handling risks associated with this task. Another way of tackling the problem is to use a fork-lift truck to move bagged products around site. This avoids the need for manual handling, almost getting rid of the risk of injury and increasing worker efficiency, so saving both time and money. For large projects it may be more appropriate to have ready-mixed cement delivered to the site.

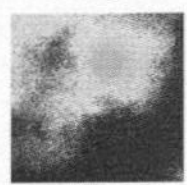

CASE STUDY 10

Fitting boiler to interior wall

Task

On a house-building project the boilers were fitted to the kitchen wall after the kitchen units had been installed by the carpenters. Each installation was carried out by a single plumbing and heating engineer. The heating engineer had to support the boiler manually and fix it to the wall while leaning across the kitchen units.

Problem

Fixing the boiler to the wall presented a manual handling risk because of the poor posture required, the restricted access and the awkwardness of supporting a load away from the body and fixing it into position at the same time. Although there were no manual handling injuries directly associated with this task, the engineer identified it as a serious manual handling problem.

Finding a solution

After consulting with other workers, the contractor agreed a simple change in the programme of works which allowed the boilers to be fixed to the wall before the kitchen units were fitted. It was agreed that, whenever possible, two workers would carry out the task - one supporting the boiler while the other fixed it to the wall. Final connections could be made at a later date.

Results

This simple but highly effective solution meant that the workers could have a much better posture and apply minimal effort during the fitting of the boiler. The handling of the boiler was much easier and a faster fixing time was achieved. Consulting with other workers about the problem made the change in the programme of works much easier to carry out. There were zero cost implications.

This case study highlights the value of consulting the workers who actually do the job, and their safety representatives.

CASE STUDY 11

Fitting external guttering

Task

Plumbing contractors traditionally fit rainwater pipes and guttering after the builder has removed the scaffolding. On one particular site the plumber had to carry all his materials up by ladder before fixing the guttering in position, working from the ladder.

Problem

This task presented a risk from manual handling because of the need to carry materials up the ladder and the poor posture required in working from the ladder. The job of fixing the guttering required a greater effort and there was a high risk of falling from the ladder. Workers were concerned about securing the ladder, the ability to climb a ladder safely while carrying materials and the hazards associated with working from a ladder.

Finding a solution

Through liaison with the principal contractor, the plumbing contractor was able to negotiate a change in the programme of works so that the rainwater pipe and guttering could be fitted before the scaffold was dropped. This required a simple change in the design of the scaffold, by the temporary works designer, to enable the downpipe to be fitted. Following consultation with the scaffolding company, this change was easily achieved. With the scaffold still in place, the plumber's materials were lifted by fork-lift truck onto the scaffold platform and the guttering was fitted from the safety of the scaffold platform.

Results

Using this solution the plumbing contractor reduced the manual handling risks associated with this task. In addition, the safety risks associated with working from ladders were also reduced.

This case emphasises the value of good planning, communication and co-operation between duty holders. Consulting workers from other trades involved in the project enabled the changes to be made with minimal disruption. Damage to the pipework and guttering by others using the scaffolding was avoided through good communication. The small additional cost in providing the scaffolding was offset by savings made due to more efficient working.

CASE STUDY 12

Placing concrete beams (lintels)

Task

As part of a large building project a contractor needed to place 150 precast reinforced concrete lintels each weighing 115 kg.

Problem

The handling of reinforced concrete lintels of this size was known to pose a serious manual handling risk. The contractor considered casting the lintels on site but the time and cost involved in the setting of the form work and reinforcement, the curing and the stripping of the form work, ruled out this approach. The contractor then estimated that to manually handle the lintels safely, five workers would be required to work together as a team and staging would need to be built at every lintel position. However, the shape and size of the lintels made safe team handling impossible. In addition to the high risk of manual handling injury this method was neither time- nor cost-efficient.

Results

The lift truck presented a simple and inexpensive solution to the manual handling problem. Its introduction onto the work site was simple and workers found the lift truck easy to operate and manoeuvre into place. This solution resulted in getting rid of almost all of the manual handling risk associated with the placing of heavy lintels.

Designers should be aware of the manual handling difficulties associated with reinforced concrete lintels and should consider specifying lightweight steel lintels where possible. Lightweight steel lintels can usually be easily positioned using a telehandler. The need for lifting equipment, such as a telehandler, should be identified at an early stage in the planning process so that its availability is planned.

Finding a solution

The contractor investigated ways to lift the lintels into place mechanically. Use of a hand-operated lift truck to raise and place the lintels was found to be the most appropriate method. The lift truck was operated by turning a handle. It took approximately 10 minutes to lift and place one lintel using this lift truck.

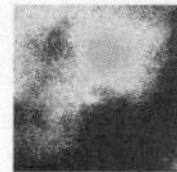

CASE STUDY 13

Transporting materials using conveyors

Task

There is often a need to clear material from sites where mechanical diggers and earth movers cannot be used. Examples include:

(a) working in culverts;

(b) existing cellar conversions which require the lowering of floor levels;

(c) carrying out construction work behind existing development.

On one particular site where the floor level of a building was being lowered, there was limited access for a mini-digger to manoeuvre and dig. As work continued, space became more limited because of the volume of excess material that had to be removed. There was no access in the building for the dumper so the material had to be moved manually out of the building using wheelbarrows.

Problem

The use of wheelbarrows presented a manual handling risk because the barrows were often overloaded and had to be pushed for considerable distances over uneven ground. In addition to manually handling heavy material, workers had to assume poor body posture to enable them to carry out their work in the confined space available.

Finding a solution

The company recognised the manual handling problems involved as well as the inefficiency of the system used. They decided to introduce powered mini-conveyors with separate self-contained units which could be readily adapted to suit their particular site conditions. As the mini-digger moved back along the length of the building, the mini-conveyors were placed in position to load material into the dumper.

Results

The risks from manual handling, although not eliminated, were reduced, particularly in areas where poor posture had been a problem. The company achieved substantial cost savings despite the hire costs of the equipment. The flexibility of the system was one of the main factors influencing its use in this case study.

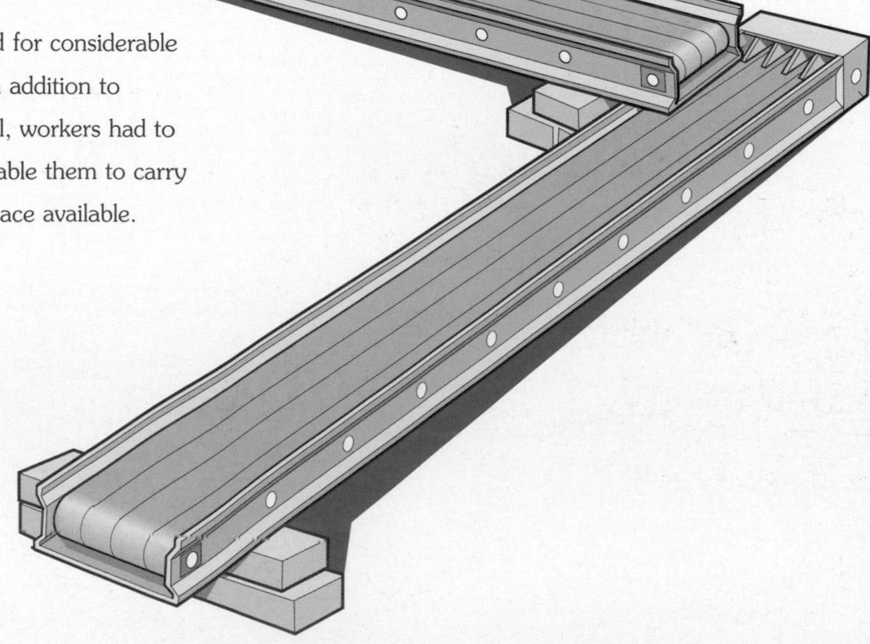

CASE STUDY 14

Bricklaying

Task

Bricklaying is a repetitive manual handling task done on almost all construction sites. Bricks are laid at various heights and bricklayers usually work continuously throughout the day with no change in activity.

Problem

Considerable bending and stooping is needed to place bricks at either high or low levels. A single brick is not heavy but there is a risk of injury from the repetitiveness of the task and the fixed, stooped working position needed to carry it out. The siting of the brick stacks and mortar often increases the amount of bending and stooping needed. Back problems are a common complaint among bricklayers.

Finding a solution

To reduce the risk of injury, this type of task needs to be carried out between waist and shoulder height. On one particular site the contractor recognised that the risk of injury could be reduced by making some small changes to the way the bricks and mortar were made available to the bricklayers. Workers on site constructed a small, stable platform on which the bricks and mortar were stacked, raising them to approximately the waist height of the bricklayers.

Results

This simple measure made sure the bricklayers had a better working position. Workers commented that this measure had also reduced the amount of energy and effort they needed to use in order to continue bricklaying throughout the day. This simple solution had minimal costs as it was constructed to suit the particular site conditions and was made from materials readily available on the site.

An additional measure which can help to improve the posture of bricklayers is the use of a 'half-lift' scaffold which, if suitably programmed into the sequence of work, can help to ensure that bricks are laid at the optimum level for the bricklayer, ie between waist and shoulder height.

CASE STUDY 15

Handling of lead flashing

Task

Rolls of lead, to be used as flashing for porches and chimneys, were delivered to a site and stored in a secure area. Their weights varied between 37 kg and 73 kg. When required for use, the lead rolls were carried by hand from the secure store to the point of use.

Problem

The handling of the lead rolls was known to pose a manual handling risk because of the heavy weights involved. Also a number of workers had complained of back problems although there were no formally reported manual handling injuries associated with this activity. The lighter rolls were carried by a single worker, the heavier ones being carried either by two workers or, if available, a dumper truck was used.

Finding a solution

The contractor had identified that this task carried a serious risk of injury and had arranged for delivery of the lead to be made as close to the storage area as possible. Because a dumper truck was not always available to move the lead, there was the possibility that workers would risk carrying rolls single-handedly, so this practice was banned under site rules. The weight of the lead was reduced by cutting it into smaller lengths where possible. Workers inserted a metal rod through the centre of the roll to form a carrying handle. This made the roll easier to handle requiring less effort. Workers were able to get a better grip on the rod and could maintain an improved posture.

Results

These combined measures, although simple, were effective in reducing the risk of injury. They also cost the contractor little as they mainly involved a change in the way the task was organised and managed. Worker involvement in developing the measures has increased their understanding of manual handling risks and has helped to prevent them from lifting and carrying other loads which are unsafe to carry on their own.

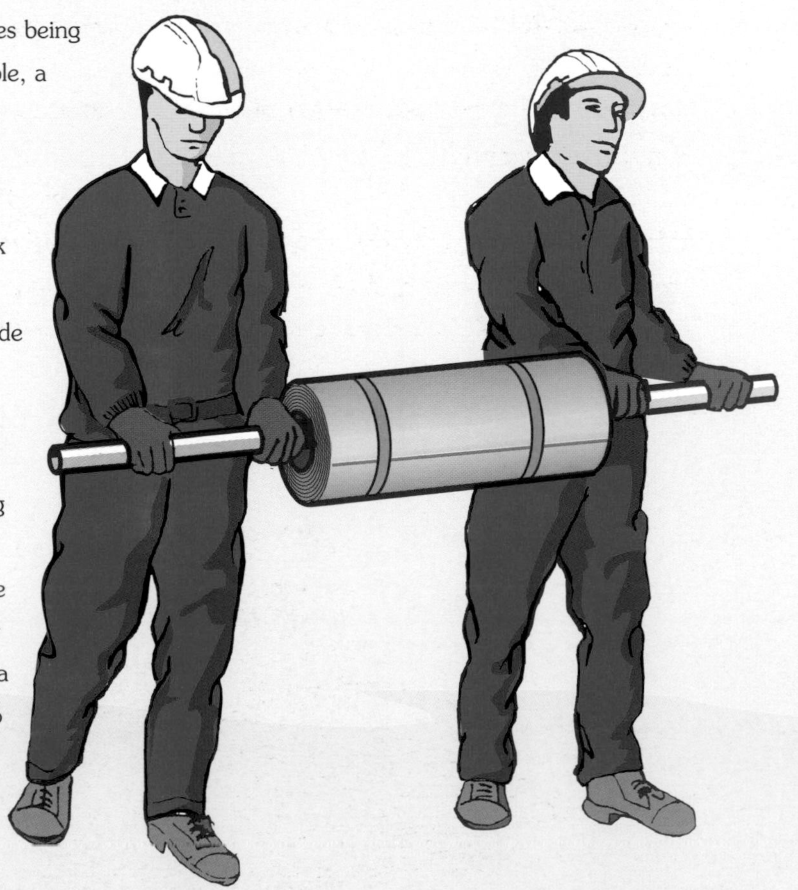

CASE STUDY 16

Laying paving blocks

Task

Decorative paving blocks are usually supplied to sites in bound packs with individual rows strapped separately. One or two of these rows of blocks are unloaded and taken to where workers are laying them.

Problem

On one particular site, labourers were required to split the pack, load the loose blocks into a wheelbarrow, transport them to their point of use and restack them ready for use by the paviours. This activity involved repetitive double handling by the labourers. Considerable bending and stooping was needed as most of the work was done at low ground level. The paviours, who were constantly supplied with blocks, continued working in a bent position without breaks or changes in activity. Both labourers and paviours complained to their site manager of back pain.

Finding a solution

The contractor introduced a block cart that was specially designed to clamp and secure a section of blocks and deliver them into position ready for laying. The contractor also made changes to the way the work was organised which meant that the paviours could take turns to supply each other with the blocks. This change of activity had similar benefits to taking a rest break as it ensured that they had a chance to vary their posture. They experienced less back pain as a result.

Results

The risk of injury to both labourers and paviours was substantially reduced. Damage to the blocks caused by continually stacking and restacking them was also reduced, resulting in savings of 5% over a year. The greater carrying capacity of the block cart compared with the wheelbarrow resulted in an increase in laying rate per gang of between 20-25%. Other labour savings were also realised which were used to offset the cost of the block cart.

Mechanised laying using vacuum or hydraulic systems to place blocks will eliminate the need for manual handling in this type of work and should be encouraged wherever possible (see *Good ideas for tackling manual handling risks*, (iv)).

CASE STUDY 17

Placing coping stones

Task

Precast coping stones, each weighing approximately 130 kg, were being manually placed onto a prepared mortar bed with a narrow joint between each stone. The work was being carried out on a major metro project with the stones being placed along the edge of the train platforms.

Problem

The change in ground level at the edge of the platforms meant that the workers placing the stones had an unstable posture with one leg higher than the other. Because of this constraint, only two workers could actually be involved in the final placing of the stones. The stones also had sharp edges making it difficult for the workers to grip them properly. The combination of the weight, the type of load and the environmental constraints meant there was a high risk of manual handling injury associated with this task.

Finding a solution

The principal contractor decided that mechanised lifting equipment would be required to reduce the potential for manual handling injury. Use of a handling device would allow the workers to lift the stones without having to bend at the waist. A vacuum powered handling device was chosen. This was battery powered rather than attached to a vacuum power pack unit and it gave the advantage of vacuum lifting with unrestricted mobility.

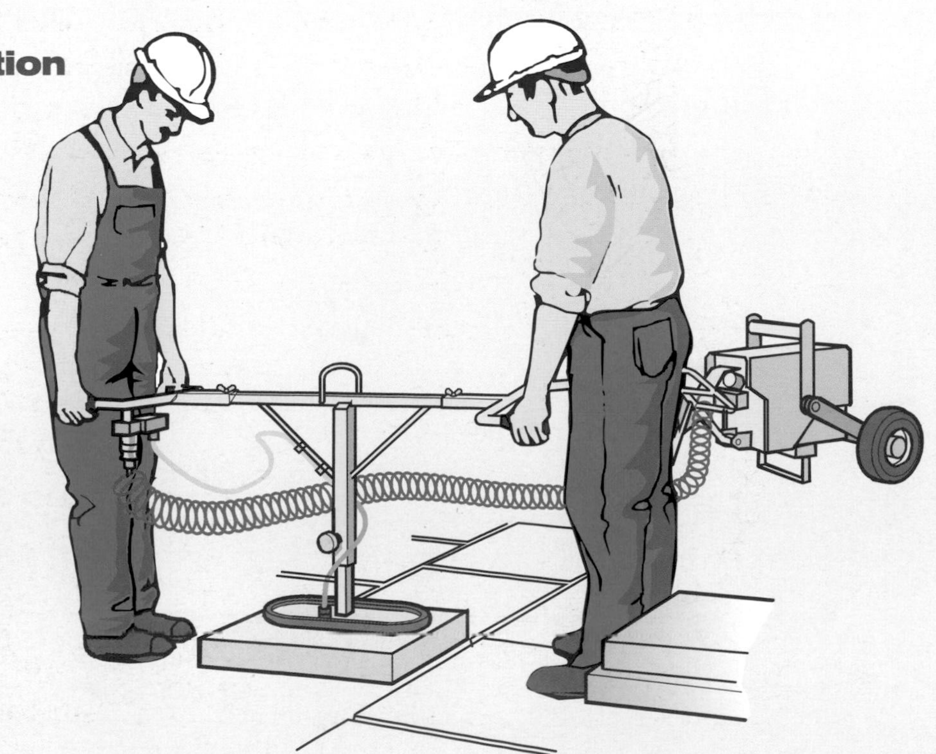

Results

The effects of using this equipment were immediate. Workers did not have to touch the stones so the risk of injury to their hands was removed. An improved lifting posture was achieved when using the device as workers did not have to bend at the waist in order to place the stones. Copings could be placed closer together without difficulty and this removed the need for jointing between them. Removing large copings from the top of the stack was made easier by using 'bicycle' style handles on the device which allowed four people to work as a team to lift the stones. Overall, the use of this equipment resulted in a safer and more efficient operation.

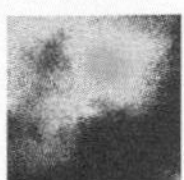

CASE STUDY 18

Placing kerbstones

Task

The stringing out and placing of concrete kerbstones each weighing about 60 kg has created manual handling problems in the industry for a long time.

Problem

On one particular contract, two-person handling of kerbstones was practised as a way of reducing the potential risk of manual handling injury. The weight of the stones and the need for two-person handling meant that the process was slow and output was considerably reduced. Workers complained of aches and pains and became tired very easily.

Finding a solution

The workers themselves, in an attempt to reduce the sheer effort they needed to do the job, tried using sack barrows to lift and place the kerbstones. They found it was relatively simple to get the stones onto the forks of the sack barrow: it required very little effort to move the load into place, and the forks were thin enough to allow the barrow to be extracted when the kerbstone had been placed.

Results

This novel use of a sack barrow, developed by the workers, vastly reduced the amount of effort needed to do the job. The workers were able to perform the entire operation very effectively by themselves and without undue strain. Up to 350 kerbstones were laid in a day by one worker, which is twice the expected output. This case study highlights the benefits of involving workers who do the job, and their safety representatives, in thinking about and developing manual handling solutions.

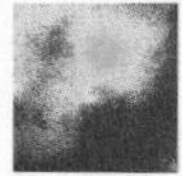

CASE STUDY 19

Handling site cabin sections

Task

A contractor built and repaired wall sections of site cabins in an in-house workshop. These sections needed to be moved around the workshop for finishing and to be stored.

Problem

Although the individual sections were not heavy and could be handled safely by two workers, the size and finish of the sections made them unwieldy and difficult to grasp. Carrying the sections around the workshop required the workers to assume awkward postures which increased the amount of strain placed on the back and upper limbs. Installing mechanical lifting equipment to move the sections was not considered practical on the grounds of cost.

Finding a solution

Recognising the problem, the workers themselves identified a cheap and simple solution which was accepted by the contractor. A small hole was drilled into each side of the timber frame of the panel. The workers then fashioned a simple handle which fitted into the holes. The cabin sections were then lifted using this handle.

Results

Providing a secure handle for the two workers to hold meant that the weight of the section could be taken with the lower hand while the upper hand provided stability. The improved grip resulted in a better lifting and carrying posture for the workers. This case study demonstrates the benefits of consulting workers who perform the task and their safety representatives when looking for solutions to manual handling problems.

CASE STUDY 20

Transporting materials over rough ground

Task

Listed and historic buildings often have limited access for today's construction machinery during refurbishment or development. This, combined with the requirement to use traditional materials, often creates multiple manual handling problems for a contractor. One particular contractor was building an extension to a small village church using traditional stone and lintels. Pallets of stone and other materials were delivered to the church and left outside the gate. They needed to be moved into the church grounds.

Problem

Getting the materials from the roadside into the church grounds posed a serious problem for the contractor. A lych-gate severely restricted the access to the grounds and ruled out the use of a fork-lift truck to move the pallets. An uneven gravel pathway from the gate to the church made it difficult to use a standard pallet truck. Carrying the materials would have been slow and presented a high risk of injury.

Finding a solution

The contractor considered laying hardboard sheeting along the length of the path so that a standard pallet truck could be used. However, this solution was rejected as it was too expensive. Unable to provide a motorised method for moving the pallets, the contractor found a pallet cart with pneumatic tyres that was specially designed for moving over rough ground.

Results

Although this solution still required manual handling to move the pallet cart, it significantly reduced the risk of injury presented by carrying the materials or from pulling the standard pallet truck over the rough ground. The solution was good value for money, acceptable to the workers and could be used to move all the materials required for the extension. The client was satisfied that the truck would not cause any damage to the church path.

CASE STUDY 21

Moving plasterboard

Task

During development of an old warehouse into housing, labourers had to move plasterboard up to the first floor of the building. Although single sheets of plasterboard were not heavy, they were flimsy and unwieldy and could act as a 'sail' in the wind which greatly increased their weight. This, and the absence of handholds, made the boards difficult to grip.

Problem

The large size of the boards, combined with having to move them within a confined space, meant that the labourers had to lift and carry them using awkward postures. Increased effort was required to control the boards while carrying them along walkways cluttered with obstacles such as electric cables, materials and litter. This increased the risk of injury both from manual handling and from slips, trips and falls.

Finding a solution

The company already had a hoist on site which they could use to lift the plasterboard up to the first floor of the building. Arrangements were made so that any new deliveries of plasterboard were made as close as possible to the hoist to reduce manual handling at this point. The contractor brought in a panel trolley which was used to take the plasterboard from the hoist to its point of use. Clearing the walkways of litter and other obstructions made access easier, reducing the effort needed to push the panel trolley along.

Results

This combination of simple, inexpensive and readily available measures effectively reduced the manual handling and other safety risks (slips, trips and falls) associated with this task. Use of the hoist and panel trolley meant that more boards could be moved at one go, reducing the number of people involved in the task. Introducing good housekeeping measures also reduced the potential fire risk on this site.

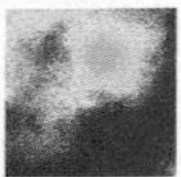

CASE STUDY 22

Handling of block pallets

Task

Building blocks, each weighing over 20 kg, were delivered to a site on pallets and lifted and moved by fork-lift truck to material lay-down areas. The blocks were secured with a single strap. Workers had to remove the strapping to unload the blocks from the pallet before taking them to their actual point of use.

Problem

During transport, the stack of blocks became unstable and likely to fall when the strapping was later removed. The potential risk of injury came not only from the blocks falling, but also from the subsequent restacking that was required. This posed a likely risk of back injury due to the size and weight of the blocks, the stooped posture of the workers and the repetitiveness involved in restacking the blocks. Other problems included damage to the blocks and time lost in restacking, which increased the contractor's costs.

Finding a solution

The site manager contacted the supplier and arranged for additional strapping to be used to provide extra stability to the blocks during transport. The cost of the additional strapping was minimal.

Results

This illustrates how manual handling and safety risks can be considerably reduced at very little cost. Both the manual handling risk associated with restacking the blocks and the safety risk from falling blocks were reduced because the extra strapping gave improved stability to the block stacks: a simple solution but highly effective. Other benefits included reduced wastage and a cleaner, tidier site. This case study is also a good example of the contractor and supplier working together to address manual handling problems.

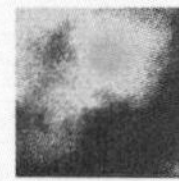

CASE STUDY 23

Prefabrication of service pipework

Task

Service pipework totalling 1750 m in length and ranging from 25 to 500 mm diameter had to be erected at height on an operational petrochemical plant.

Problem

Working at height, operatives had to carry out multiple operations involving manual handling over prolonged periods inside the operational plant.

Finding a solution

The manual handling difficulties associated with this job were identified at the concept design stage. It was decided to fabricate the pipework and associated services within a number of modular steel structures. The major fabrication work could then be carried out more easily and to a higher standard within a controlled environment off site.

Results

The design change to prefabricated modules resulted in a vast reduction in the number of manual handling operations at height. The number of site lifting operations by crane was also reduced. The 1750 m of pipework was erected within five days, resulting in a major cost saving.

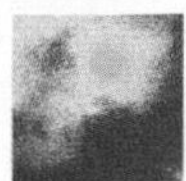

CASE STUDY 24

Replacement of bridge, motorway and trunk road signs

Task

Old, corroded and out-of-date road signs on bridges, motorways and trunk roads needed to be removed and replaced with new ones.

Problem

The road signs were both heavy and bulky, making manual handling very difficult. Two workers were required to manually remove the old signs, lift the new signs from the lorry and position them onto the posts at the roadside. A significant number of manual handling injuries were reported to the contractor.

Finding a solution

A special lifting beam was developed that was capable of fitting all types of posts. The beam was fitted over the post and locked into position from a mobile elevated work platform. Ropes were fitted to the sign with special brackets so that the old sign could be released, removed from its post and lowered to the ground. The new sign was then attached to the beam and raised into position. This procedure got rid of the need for manual handling of the signs.

Results

The beam manufacture and testing costs were approximately £400. This was considered highly cost-effective in reducing manual handling risks and subsequent complaints of injury as well as reducing the plant requirements for the job.

CASE STUDY 25

Placing road signs on a motorway

Task

Road signs for traffic management had to be placed on a motorway central reserve. The signs and the frames for holding them in place had to be carried across the live carriageway, positioned on the central reserve and weighted down with sandbags.

Problem

A single A-frame and a sign each weighs more than 20 kg. For safety reasons each piece of equipment had to carried single-handedly across the carriageway. In addition, sandbags to weight down the assembled signs also had to be carried over. A number of manual handling incidents had been reported and the company was increasingly concerned about the safety aspects of making multiple carriageway crossings to complete the job. Although the number of accidents to workers on high-speed roads is relatively low, the consequences of such accidents can be very serious.

Finding a solution

Having identified the manual handling problem, the contractor arranged to have an aluminium adapter made that would fit onto the post of the crash barrier. This resulted in a reduction in the size of frame needed for the signs and reduced its weight to less than half of the weight of the original A-frame used. The frame and sign were also constructed from aluminium to further reduce the weight to be manually handled. These changes were agreed with the client.

Results

The use of lighter, aluminium frames and signs made it easier for individual workers to carry the loads across the carriageway, significantly reducing the risk from manual handling. The need for sandbags to weight the frames was removed, so both the number of loads and the number of crossings were reduced. In many cases, the frames will remain in place on the central reserve so that any sign changes that need to be made at a later date will require only one handling operation.

The cost of a single reusable adapter was approximately £8, making this an inexpensive yet highly effective way of reducing a serious manual handling problem and at the same time improving the safety of a dangerous activity.

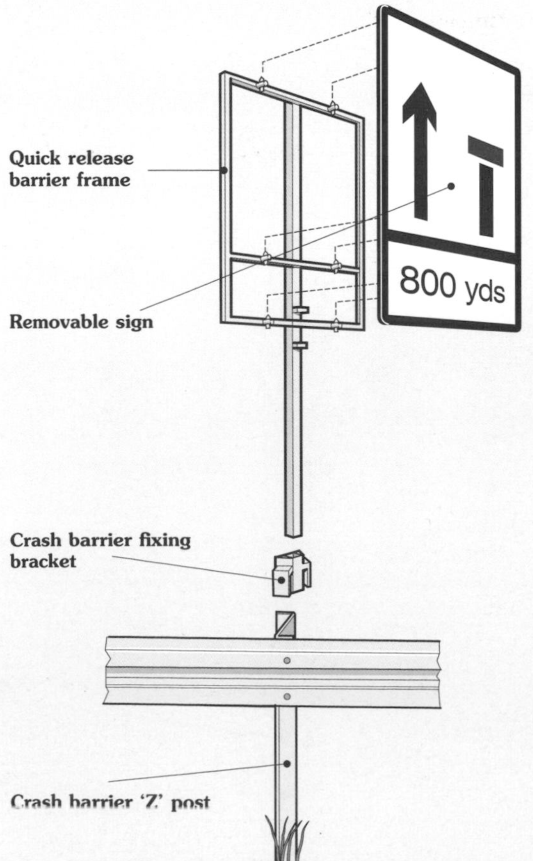

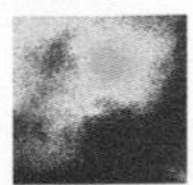

CASE STUDY 26

Ground treatment of open-faced road tunnel

Task

A drainage tunnel required major ground treatment work in order to stabilise it when the ground conditions changed unexpectedly. Horizontal bore holes had to be drilled and then filled with a special grout.

Problem

A large number of bore holes had to be drilled in order to stabilise the wall of the tunnel. The bore holes were made using hand-held drilling equipment which weighed about 50 kg. The drilling equipment had to be moved manually into position for each bore hole and held in position while the drilling was carried out. In addition to the heavy weight of the equipment being handled, the work had to be done in cramped conditions.

Finding a solution

The contractor considered the manual handling risks from this operation to be unacceptably high. To prevent the manual handling problems associated with the drilling operations, a hydraulically driven automated system was designed. A drill was fitted to a hydraulic arm that was capable of rotating 180° on the east-west axis and 45° on the north-south axis.

Results

As well as removing manual handling from this job, the introduction of the automated system also reduced or got rid of other health risks, such as exposure to noise, vibration and silica dust. The design, manufacture and testing of the arm and the drill were costed at £65 000, representing 3.5% of the total cost of the grouting operation.

The introduction of the hydraulic arm substantially contributed to the early completion of the job because it was faster, easier and more accurate to use.

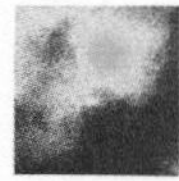

CASE STUDY 27

Transporting LPG cylinders across carriageways

Task

Liquid petroleum gas (LPG) gas cylinders have often been used to light road signs. Large cylinders can weigh more than 55 kg. On one contract, two workers were each required to carry one of the large cylinders across a live carriageway to light signs on the central reserve.

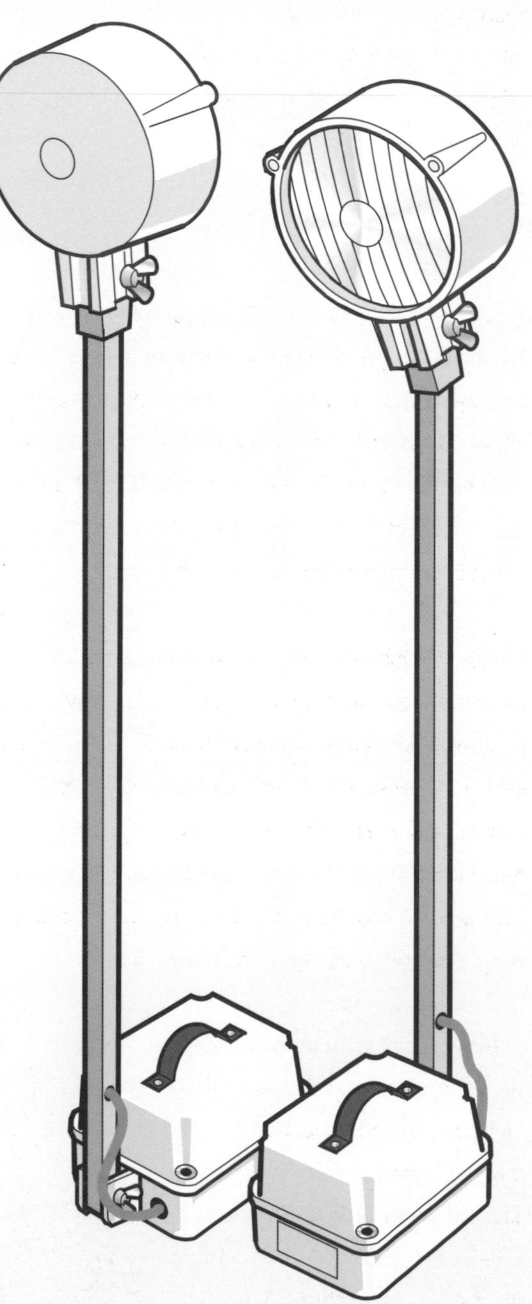

Problem

Transporting the LPG cylinders across the carriageway posed a serious risk of manual handling injury to the workers involved. There were also considerable safety implications involved in carrying such heavy loads across the live carriageway.

Finding a solution

Because the contract was only short term, the contractor opted to use battery-powered electric lighting, weighing less than 10 kg, to light the signs.

Results

The use of these lights almost got rid of the risk of manual handling injury as they weigh much less than LPG cylinders. The use of battery-powered electric lighting is particularly suitable for short-term work. Where the work is likely to be long term, use of a mains electrical supply to power the lights should be considered. Consideration could also be given to the use of diamond-grade signs with higher reflectivity.

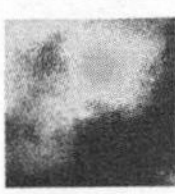

Good ideas for tackling manual handling risks

(i) Programming the early installation of stairways so that they can be used for access during the building works has a number of benefits. The effort and time involved in moving both loads and people from one level to another is reduced, as the stairs allow the movement of equipment and materials between floors.

(ii) Forming ceilings with sheet materials can involve two workers working on tower scaffolds trying to support the sheet in place (normally with the head) while fixing it in position. Use of a panel lifter allows a single worker to lift, position and support the sheet and then fix it. Except for placing the sheet on the panel lifter, manual handling is removed.

(iii) Raising rebar sections to waist height on trestles enables workers to assume an improved body posture while tying. Once completed, the sections can be stiffened using scaffold tubes to prevent excessive flexing. When lifted into place using a mechanical lifting aid, the scaffold tubes are removed. This method has the added advantage of keeping the rebar clear of muddy ground during tying.

(iv) Use of vacuum or hydraulic systems to place kerbstones, slabs or blocks removes nearly all manual handling from the task. These systems can be supplied as adapters connecting to existing plant (such as earth-moving machinery) which may already be on site. Use of paving slab lifting devices also reduces risks from bending and lifting.

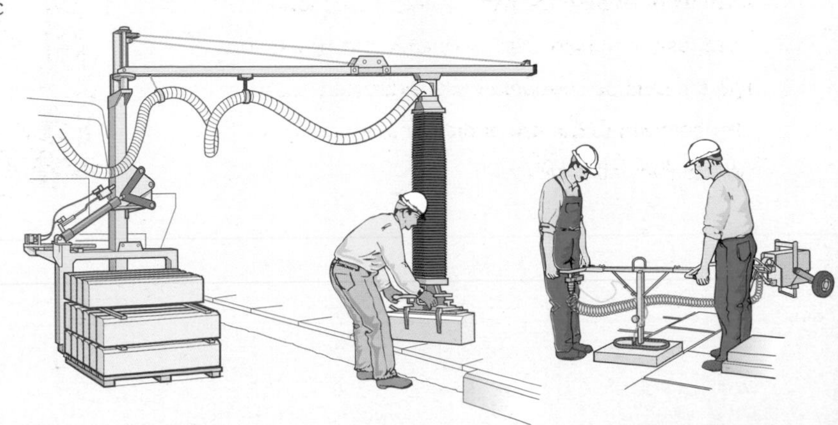

(v) To transport sheet materials use panel trolleys where possible. For manual handling of other large items, a variety of devices are available, including magnetic grips, suction grips, plate carriers and handling slings.

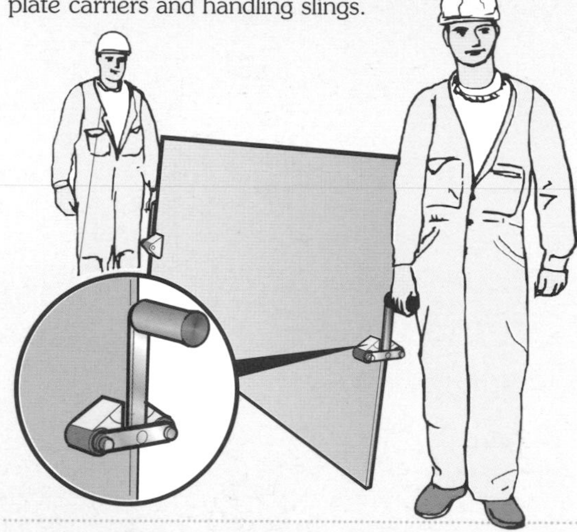

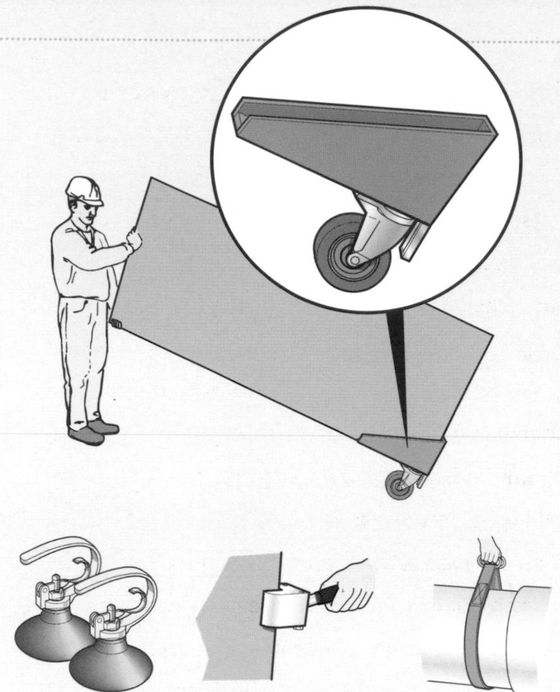

(vi) Instead of using traditional timber stud work or masonry walls to construct internal partitions, a lightweight metal framework system can be used. This greatly reduces the loads which need to be manually handled. There are also other benefits of using such a system. They occupy less floor space than the traditional formats and the reduced weight can mean savings in the structural design. Any problems with reduced sound insulation can be overcome with good technical design.

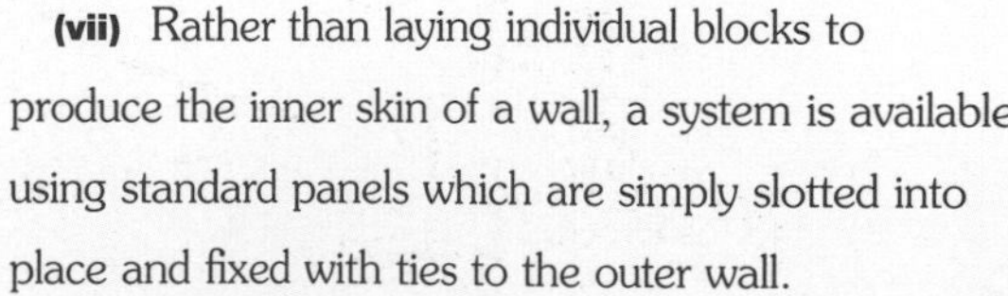

(vii) Rather than laying individual blocks to produce the inner skin of a wall, a system is available using standard panels which are simply slotted into place and fixed with ties to the outer wall.

(viii) A study of the efficiency of blocklayers has shown that their workload can be reduced by 20% by using blocks with hollows into which the hand or the thumb can be inserted. This allows the block to be gripped more easily. Worker performance was shown to increase by 17%. Strain on the lower back was reduced and worker satisfaction and quality of work increased as well.

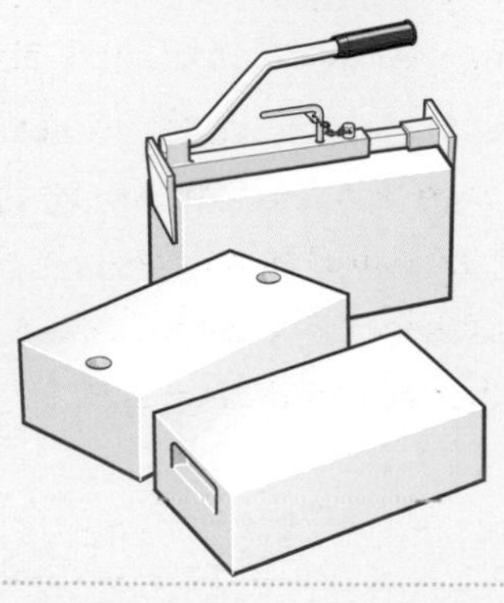

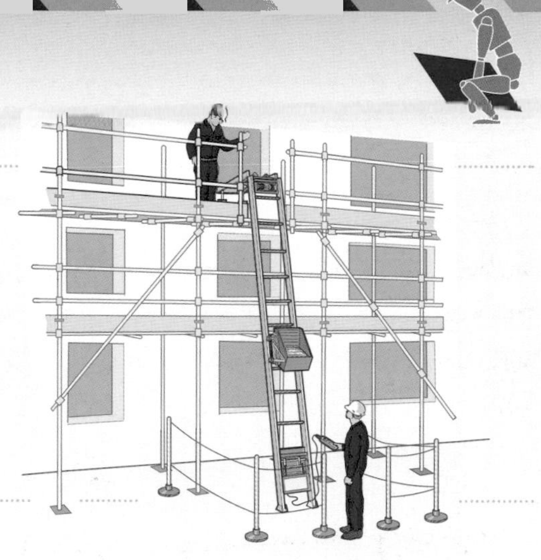

(ix) Ladder hoists are available to hire or buy. It is possible to adapt the hoist to take a wide variety of materials. Adjustable angle track sections and accessories enable the materials to be transported onto pitched roofs or through window openings into buildings.

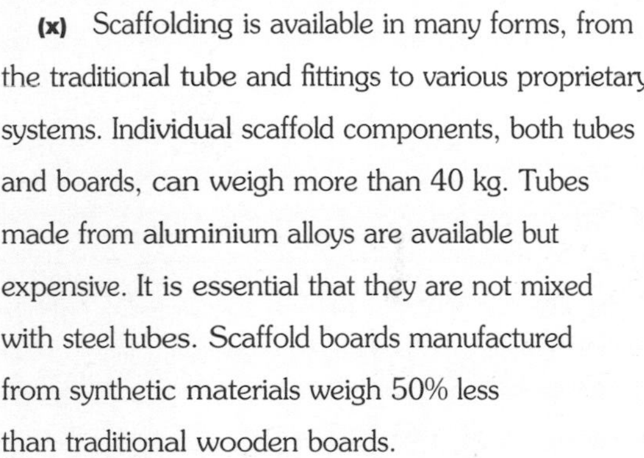

(x) Scaffolding is available in many forms, from the traditional tube and fittings to various proprietary systems. Individual scaffold components, both tubes and boards, can weigh more than 40 kg. Tubes made from aluminium alloys are available but expensive. It is essential that they are not mixed with steel tubes. Scaffold boards manufactured from synthetic materials weigh 50% less than traditional wooden boards.

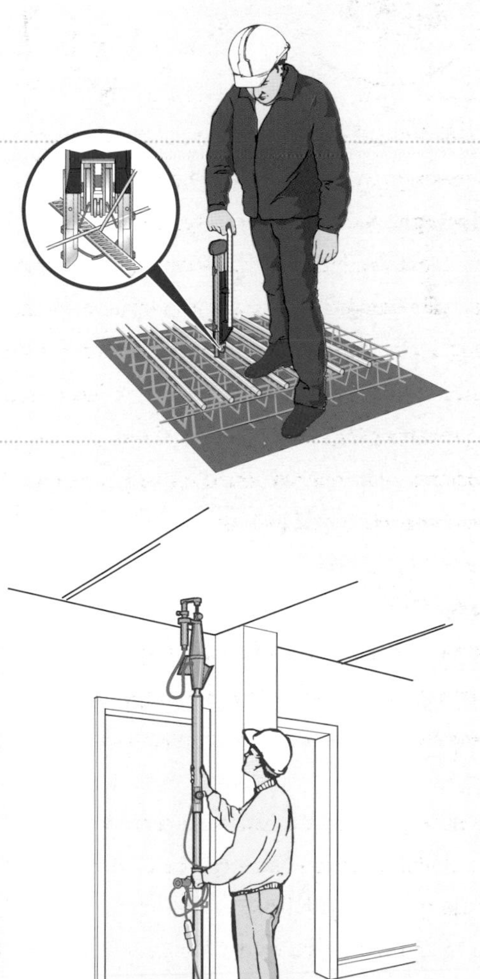

(xi) Normal tying of rebar involves repeated poor posture being assumed by the worker (especially when tying at ground level) and a repetitive twisting action of the wrist. Automatic tying using a special tool requires 'pull' rather than 'twisting' action and can improve body posture.

(xii) Installing hangers for ductwork, cable trays, etc, requires repeated drilling into the ceiling. Usually the fitter stands on a ladder or trestle supporting the drill vertically above shoulder height. As well as the force required to drill into the concrete, a high static workload is placed upon the worker. A telescopic spring-loaded mounting can be used to hold the drill in position and allow it to be operated remotely. This increases the rate at which a number of holes can be drilled and is also safer and less strenuous. Arranging the fixing positions on a grid location in preassembled units also provides a means for fixing as well as providing a weakened area to form a knockout point for service access, thus saving the need for drilling either up or down.

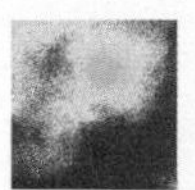

APPENDIX 1

Principal legal requirements

Health and Safety at Work etc Act 1974 requires:

- employers and self-employed workers to ensure they provide and maintain workplaces, equipment and systems of work that are, so far as is reasonably practicable, safe to workers and the public;
- designers and suppliers to ensure their products may be used safely;
- employees to take care of their own and others' health and safety.

Construction (Design and Management) Regulations 1994 apply to all stages of a construction project and place duties on clients, designers and contractors. The Regulations aim to ensure the:

- selection of competent appointees and provision of adequate resources;
- reduction of risk at the design and planning stages of a project;
- effective management of health and safety throughout the project.

Construction (Health, Safety and Welfare) Regulations 1996 contain specific Regulations that impact on manual handling:

- arrangements should be made to provide protection against adverse weather;
- arrangements should be made to ensure adequate lighting;
- the site should be kept reasonably clean and in good order.

Management of Health and Safety at Work Regulations 1992 require employers and self-employed workers to:

- identify the measures they need to take by carrying out risk assessments;
- institute safety management systems;
- appoint persons to assist in health and safety management;
- ensure co-ordination and co-operation;
- make emergency procedures;
- provide information and relevant training to employees.

Manual Handling Operations Regulations 1992 are designed specifically to eliminate manual handling risks or, if this is not possible, to reduce risks to acceptable levels. The Regulations require employers and self-employed workers to:

- avoid manual handling operations so far as is reasonably practicable;
- carry out a risk assessment of those manual handling activities that cannot be avoided;
- take appropriate steps to reduce the risk to health to the lowest level reasonably practicable.

Health and Safety (Consultation with Employees) Regulations 1996 require employers to consult with workers, either directly or indirectly through elected representatives of employee safety, on matters relating to their health and safety at work.

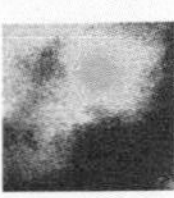

Acknowledgements

The Health and Safety Executive acknowledges the generosity of the following companies who supplied case studies to help compile this publication:

Amey
Bickerton Group plc
Bovis Homes Limited – Central Region
Bryant Group Services Limited
Crown House Engineering
Drillfix AG
Galliford plc – Safety Department
Hallmark Developments Limited
HSS Lift & Shift – part of the HSS Hire Service Group plc
Kier North East – part of the Kier Group
John Laing plc
Latimer Contracting Limited
Lignacite Limited
Mace Limited
Marshalls Panablok (UK) Limited
Matholite Products Limited
Norwest Holst Limited
Project Services (UK) Ltd
Rako Products Limited
Tilbury Douglas Construction Limited – Building Division
Twigden Homes Limited – part of the Kier Group
Vincents (Norwich) Limited
Wallis Limited – part of the Kier Group
Warings Contractors Ltd

Photographers:
Stephen Sandon – Building Services Journal
J A Hewes (Photographers) – Southsea

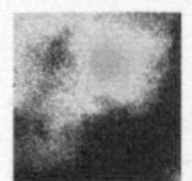

References

Manual handling. Manual Handling Operations Regulations 1992. Guidance on Regulations L23 HSE Books 1998 ISBN 0 7176 2415 3

Selecting a health and safety consultancy INDG133 HSE Books 1992

Health and safety in construction HSG150 HSE Books 1996 ISBN 0 7176 1143 4

Designing for health and safety in construction HSE Books 1995 ISBN 0 7176 0807 7

Further reading and sources of advice

HSE priced publications

Management of Health and Safety at Work Regulations 1992. Approved Code of Practice L21 HSE Books 1992 ISBN 0 7176 1412 8 (New edition in production)

Manual handling: Solutions you can handle HSG115 HSE Books 1994 ISBN 0 7176 0693 7

Managing construction for health and safety. Construction (Design and Management) Regulations 1994 L54 HSE Books 1995 ISBN 0 7176 0792 5

A guide to managing health and safety in construction HSE Books 1995 ISBN 0 7176 0755 0

HSE free publications

Getting to grips with manual handling: a short guide for employers INDG143 HSE Books 1993 (Available in priced packs, ISBN 0 7176 0966 9)

The Construction (Health, Safety and Welfare) Regulations 1996 INDG220 HSE Books 1999 (Available in priced packs, ISBN 0 7176 1161 2)

Handling heavy building blocks CIS37(rev) HSE Books 1999

Consulting employees on health and safety: A guide to the law INDG232 HSE Books 1996 (Available in priced packs, ISBN 0 7176 1615 0)

Other publications

Managing materials and components on site CIRIA 1998 Special publication 146 ISBN 086017 481 6

While every effort has been made to ensure the accuracy of the references listed in this publication, their future availability cannot be guaranteed.

Printed and published by the Health and Safety Executive 1/00 C120